Legends of Fitness
The Forces, Influencers, and Innovations
That Helped Shape the Fitness Industry

Stephen Tharrett, M.S.
Frank O'Rourke
James A. Peterson, Ph.D.

ISBN: 978-1-60679-166-0
Library of Congress Control Number: 2011924043
Cover design: Roger W. Rybkowski
Book layout: Bean Creek Studio

Healthy Learning
P.O. Box 1828
Monterey, CA 93942
www.healthylearning.com

"The true past departs not; no truth or goodness realized by man ever dies; or can die; but all is still here, through endless changes."
— Thomas Carlyle
1795–1881

Augie Nieto is one of the greatest leaders I've known. Everything he envisioned for the industry and his company became a reality, which is pretty amazing when you think about it.

Al Fuller, a friend and colleague, once said what makes Augie a great leader is how much he is willing to share of himself with everyone else.

I agree. He gives everyone his energy, his passion for the business, and his desire to win. Further, he empowers people and encourages them to step out of their comfort zone to create something truly noteworthy and innovative.

In reality, Life Fitness was and is an extension of Augie's personality and leadership quality. Under his guiding hand, the company created innovative, cutting-edge products because employees knew they had Augie's support to push beyond the accepted norm. They knew that no matter what, Augie would be there to celebrate their success or pick them up, dust them off, and send them back into the game.

For me, personally, it is his constant desire to celebrate successes that makes Augie stand out as a leader. It is this recognition and celebration that helps everyone around him push a little harder and reach a little farther.

Augie's Quest is yet another extension of his amazing qualities. He has shared himself at a level that exceeds his generosities of the past. By doing so, he has rallied together a tremendous group of people to create opportunities for those fighting ALS that couldn't have been envisioned a decade ago.

When you are in the presence of a exceptional leader, anything is possible. With all Augie has done, I think his greatest accomplishments are still to come, as he pushes all of us to find new ways to combat ALS.

I love you Augie,

Christopher Clawson
President
Life Fitness

WHAT WE LIVE FOR

Dedication

Acknowledgments

I want to acknowledge the many talented, innovative, and passionate professionals who have dedicated their life to enriching the lives of millions through fitness. I particularly want to thank the people who initially inspired me to pursue a life of fitness, and to share it with others, individuals such as John Sofie, former New Jersey heavyweight weightlifting champion and bodybuilder; Win Franklin, owner of Win Franklin's Gym in Plainfield, N.J.; Chuck Sipes, former Mr. Universe; Bill Pearl, former Mr. Universe; Dee Edington, Ph.D, professor at the University of Michigan; Rudy Riska, former manager of the Downtown Athletic Club in New York; James Peterson, Ph.D., my friend and colleague; John McCarthy, former Executive Director of IHRSA. I also want to extend my thanks to the numerous fitness professionals, both in the U.S. and globally, whose passion for the industry and for helping others inspires me to continue on in this industry. I also want to extend a special thanks to John Wood of oldtimestrongmen.com for helping provide pictures for the book and for reviewing our content and Bill Pearl for his contribution of pictures and photos. Lastly, I must thank my father, who always encouraged and supported my frequent exploits in the area of competitive bodybuilding, powerlifting, and weightlifting.

— Stephen Tharrett

I would like to express my gratitude to Raymond Long in Deland, Florida; David Landau of Miami, Florida; and Hillis Lake of Gainesville, Florida; and a special thanks to Thomas Plummer of Cape Cod, Massachusetts, who educated me on the Business of Fitness more than anyone. To my friends and colleagues who listened to me, as I shared my passion for this project, thank you for your patience and understanding. I would particularly like to thank Les Wiehe, who introduced me to the publisher of this book, as well as acknowledge the efforts of Tracy Maloney who supported me along the way. Jessica Stubbs, who went to considerable trouble to provide the background research and sourcing of the information for my sections of the book, thank you. You made my job considerably easier. Lastly, and most importantly, I would like to thank my co authors Stephen Tharrett and Jim Peterson, for their addition of major historical events and sections to the book. It was an honor to work with two individuals who have done so much for the health and fitness industry; their help was greatly appreciated.

— Frank O'Rourke

I want to acknowledge the passion of Frank O'Rourke for this project. His inexorable enthusiasm for this book was both infectious and unrelenting. As such, Frank's passion served as the foundation for the collective hours spent by Steve, Frank, and myself that ultimately turned Frank's dream into a reality. I'd also like to acknowledge the exceptional efforts of Steve Tharrett on this book. Having had the opportunity to work with Steve several times over the years, I have always found him to be the consummate professional. This book is no exception.

— James A. Peterson

What an extraordinary achievement this book is! Until now, no one has dared to write a history of the fitness industry from its earliest formative period to its current global situation. Nor has anyone been more qualified to write such a history from the perspective of the men and women who built this industry into what it has become today.

To the authors—to Stephen Tharrett, Jim Peterson, and Frank O'Rourke—may I say simply this: please take a bow. The worldwide fitness industry is indebted to you.

Why is this book important?

First, because it tracks the industry back to its origins and forward to its most recent developments. No one has ever attempted such an endeavor before.

Second, because the authors—Stephen Tharrett, Frank O'Rourke, and Jim Peterson—are themselves industry "insiders." For the last 40 years, they have participated in the global expansion of the industry. Because they know personally many of the industry's most influential thinkers and leaders, they have an insider's perspective as to what have been the most important and most significant factors in its development.

Third, until now, the thousands of young men and women from around the world who enter the industry each year have had no single text that could provide them with the history of the industry into which they are planning to build their careers. This text provides them with invaluable insight into the entrepreneurial evolution of the business.

Fourth, today, throughout the world, hundreds of colleges and universities are preparing young men and women for professional careers in this industry. Until now, these academic programs did not have a single textbook with which to introduce their students to the historical development of the industry. Finally, that textbook has arrived.

Fifth, from an international perspective, this industry, in less than 100 years, has become a global economic and cultural force of ever-increasing magnitude. For cultural and business historians, this text provides insight into one of the world's newest, fastest growing, and most vibrant industries.

Sixth, as is becoming ever more apparent, this industry has a vital role to play in maintaining and improving the health of every man, woman and child on the globe. Tharrett, O'Rourke, and Peterson detail the remarkable story of how this industry has re-oriented itself so as to become an indispensible component of preventive and curative health strategies. As the saying so aptly states: "Exercise is medicine."

Finally, because this text is, as its authors will willingly admit, a groundbreaking event, it will inevitably become the inspiration and launching pad for countless more efforts that will dig even deeper into the history of this industry. In the process, this text will serve as the framework for further development.

Foreword

The authors of this book have decided to dedicate this text to one of the industry's most inspirational and influential leaders—Augie Nieto, the founder and longtime CEO of Life Fitness, the world's largest and most successful fitness equipment company.

In 1980, while still a student at Claremont Men's College in California, Augie Nieto, the son of immigrant parents, joined Ray Wilson's fledgling firm, Lifecycle. Augie immediately became the new company's driving force. Traveling from fitness center to fitness center and from coast to coast, Augie became the company's first and foremost salesman of what was to become the company's signature product, the industry's first computerized exercise bicycle, (the Life Cycle).

From those humble beginnings, Augie Nieto purchased Lifecycle and transformed it into Life Fitness, which then became a dominant force in the ever-expanding fitness equipment industry. Without question, Augie has been the guiding light and inspiration behind the origin of scores of other fitness companies, national and international, which have sought to follow in the path that he had blazed.

Few people realize that as early as 1982, Augie understood more clearly than anyone else the international implications of the business and industry in which he was involved. Starting in Europe, then moving on to Asia, the Middle East, and Latin America, he became the mentor and inspiration for the development and expansion of thousands of health and fitness clubs throughout the world.

Wherever he went, Augie Nieto was always and everywhere "pro industry." He knew that if the industry grew, his business would grow. In the process, in country after country and in continent after continent, Augie was the initiator of forums and seminars that brought together the leaders of the industry so that they could motivate and challenge one another to further expand their businesses.

Little more than five years ago, while still in his mid 40s, Augie Nieto was struck down with ALS, Lou Gehrig's disease. True to his great heart and entrepreneurial spirit, he decided to devote the rest of his life to raising money for research on how to control and ultimately eliminate this terrible affliction.

Truth be known, the authors could not have dedicated this magnificent text to a more deserving individual. Its words ring true to both Augie's indomitable spirit and his noteworthy quest (Augie's quest—http://www.augiesquest.org).

— John McCarthy

The following individuals contributed their time and expertise to review this book for content accuracy. The authors would like to express their heartfelt grataitude to each of these four outstanding professionals for their contributions to this book.

Rick Caro, MBA

Rick is the President of Management Vision, a New York, New York-based consulting firm serving the health/fitness facility industry. Rick is one of the original founders of IHRSA, a former IHRSA board member and president, and one of the foremost experts in the fitness industry. His company, Management Vision is widely recognized as one of the leading global consulting firms in the health/fitness industry.

Norm Cates

Norm is the publisher of Club Insider News, an industry-leading publication that has been in existance since 1993. Norm is one of the original founders of IHRSA, as well as its first president. Prior to starting Club Insider News, Norm owned and operated clubs in Atlanta, Georgia.

Chuck Leve

Chuck is currently the executive director of the Association of Fitness Industry Retailers and Manufacturers (AFIRM). Prior to founding AFIRM, Chuck served as the vice-president of business development for IHRSA, one of several positions he held with IHRSA from the time of its inception. Prior to his tenure with IHRSA, Chuck served as the executive director of the National Court Club Association (NCCA).

John Wood

John is the founder of oldtimestrongman.com, a website dedicated to the sharing of information and training techniques developed by the strongmen of the 19th and early 20th centuries. John's website is committed to sharing with future generations the wisdom of physical culture and strength development, as practiced by the strongman of old. In addition, his website provides historical facts and information about the culture of physical training and strength development, including rare photos and pictures of the first gymnasiums, fitness equipment, and feats of strength.

Content Reviewers

Disclaimer

The authors recognize that history is composed not just of facts, but also of perspectives. Indeed, history represents the accumulation of individual perspectives about certain events, and that each perspective provides a unique glimpse into what actually occurred. As a result, what one individual deems to be a historic event, another might deem differently.

In researching the information for this book, the authors have referenced numerous sources, including books, web sites, magazine articles, newspaper articles, and interviews with individuals who were actually participants in the historical events being researched. In addition, the authors have called on their own personal recollection of events experienced during their lifetime. While our research was extensive, it was not exhaustive in every instance. As a result we may not have been privy to every relevant source pertaining to a particular occurrence. Therefore, certain historical events may not be documented or recalled in this text exactly as others remember them. Furthermore, in the industry there may be instances in this book when we felt a specific event, innovation or individual held significant historical value that other historians or professionals in the industry would question our interpretation or assessment of the historical relevance of the situation.

We offer our apologies if we have overlooked anything of historical significance in the industry in the course of authoring this book. While, we do not claim to be the foremost authorities on the history of the fitness industry, we have done our best to identify what we believe reflect the noteworthy events, individuals and innovations that have significantly influenced the course of the global fitness industry. We invite anyone reading this book who has information that might enhance the authenticity of this book (i.e., thereby providing a more accurate, comprehensive, and insightful history of certain events, individuals or innovations) to submit it to the authors (via the publisher) for possible inclusion in any future editions of this book.

Contents

The primary goal of this book is to detail the history of the health and fitness industry, touching on the individuals who have had a noteworthy impact on the industry and to highlight the equipment innovations that have played such an important role in the evolution of the industry.

In 1918, Proust, A l'ombs des jeunes filles en fleurs, said, *"What we call our future is the shadow that our past projects in front of us."* Unfortunately, unless an individual is extremely observant, shadows can go unobserved, and as a result, lessons go unlearned, innovations get lost, and mistakes get repeated. In reality, the insights and experiences of the legends, influencers, and innovators offer a glimpse into the individual's past, as well as its future.

The authors firmly believe that only by understanding the past, can individuals fully comprehend and overcome the challenges facing the industry, and more importantly, create a viable pathway for it to prosper in the future. It is our belief that learning about the past innovations, mistakes, and successes of those individuals in the fitness equipment and facility industry can help facilitate the development (and in some instances, the redevelopment) of innovative tools and programs that will ensure the continuous growth of the industry.

We have developed this book by focusing on three core subject areas that impacted the history of the fitness industry. First, we wanted to provide insight into the artisans and professionals who had a noteworthy degree of influence in helping shape the fitness industry. Second, we choose to explore the equipment innovations that we consider as having had the most influence in determining how the fitness experience has been delivered to the public. Lastly, we wanted to provide insight on the facilities and health/fitness clubs that in our opinion have become the "meccas" of fitness over the course of the industry's history.

To help bring each of these three core subject areas to light, the book is divided into 11 chapters, the first seven of which are dedicated to a different period in the history of the fitness industry. Chapter 8 details some of the exceptional individuals who have helped make the industry into a viable delivery platform for the innumerable benefits of purposeful movement. Chapters 9 and 10 look at the equipment innovations, companies, and facilities that helped shape the industry. The 11th and final chapter offers a compilation of testimonies about Augie Nieto from prominent members of the fitness industry.

It is our sincere hope that the information contained in this text will help bring forth the next generation of industry legends, influencers, and innovators, as well the next series of exceptional equipment innovations and tools.

Preface

The Fitness Industry Is Born

(Pre-Nineteenth Century)

Chapter 1

"If we could give every individual the right amount of nourishment and exercise, not too little, and not to much, we would have found the safest way to health."

— Hippocrates 460–377 B.C.

The Birth of Fitness as Art and Sport

Where It All Began

When did human movement and physical activity become fitness and sport? The earliest records of mankind indicate that around 2100 B.C., Egyptians formally introduced structured acrobatics, and its related training to the world. The Egyptians saw acrobatics as a form of both sport, and entertainment, while those who practiced it realized that to perform at a high level, it was necessary to follow a structured regiment of physical training. During this period, acrobatics was practiced by a select few, and never became a part of ordinary peoples' daily routines rather exercise became the specialty of a select few. Shortly after the Egyptians introduced acrobatics, it is believed the Chinese introduced Cong Fu. The Chinese saw Cong Fu, as it was known then, as a means of enhancing health, through the integration of breathing and formalized fluid movements of the body. Cong Fu, like the acrobatics of the Egyptian's, became the reverend ground of specialists, handed down from generation to generation by those masters entrusted to maintain the purity of the art.

The Influence of the Greeks on Exercise

One of the consequences of these regular competitions was the discovery that to be successful, the competitors had to train on a regular basis.

Over 1300 years later, in 776 B.C., the Greeks introduced sport, competition based on pitting men against each other in acts of physical prowess. The initial manifestation of these competitions, commonly referred to as the first Olympiad, was composed of one short foot race. Over the next 1,100 years, ending around 393 C.E., the Greeks introduced numerous additional physical competitions, including running events of short and long distance, throwing events, rope climbing, tumbling, and combat arts (e.g., boxing, pankration, wrestling). One of the consequences of these regular competitions was the discovery that to be successful, the competitors had to train on a regular basis. The Greeks therefore created various physical activity regimes that would benefit the performance of the participants in the various competitive events. Thus, many of the modern callisthenic movements were born. As happened with the Egyptians and Chinese, these physical activity practices were deemed as the privilege of a few, rather than a practice of the many. Interestingly, the Greeks saw prowess in feats of physical strength and endurance not just as sport, but also as a celebration of religious activity. At the peak of the Greek civilization, physical activity was seen as educational, martial (i.e., having to do with the military and fighting), and restorative (i.e.., helping to restore the natural state of the human body and soul). The Greeks introduced physical training as the central element in their post-elementary education system. Unfortunately, by the 5th century, the focus of the Greeks on physical prowess gave way to more sedate forms of body restoration, such as hot baths and spas. Concurrently, with this evolution in what was considered restorative health practices, was the fall of the Olympic Games, and with it a period of near extinction for the pursuits of physical culture among the citizens of the world.

Interestingly, it wasn't just the need to excel in the sports arena that helped drive the establishment of structured physical culture, but it was also the influence of medicine that helped shape how physical activity was perceived by the ancient Greeks. Hippocrates, a renowned Greek physician and the individual responsible for the physician's Hippocratic Oath, was among the first individuals who espoused the value of physical movement for health. Hippocrates believed strongly in the importance of proper nutrition and exercise as a form of preventive medicine and a viable pathway to good health. The following quotes from Hippocrates summarize his belief in the inherent value of physical activity:

"Walking is man's best medicine."

"If we could give every individual the right amount of nourishment and exercise, not too little, and not to much, we would have the safest way to health."

Hippocrates was not the only noteworthy individual who was an advocate for the importance of being physically active. The great philosophers of Greek culture also encouraged citizens to pursue an active lifestyle. Plato, for example, a contemporary of Hippocrates, also believed that exercise was essential. Plato's philosophy is expressed eloquently by his following statement:

"Lack of activity destroys the good condition of every human being, while movement and methodical physical exercise save and preserve it."

Hippocrates, a renowned Greek physician, was among the first individuals who espoused the value of physical movement for health.

A number of the great philosophers of Greek culture encouraged citizens to pursue an active lifestyle, including Plato.

Equipment Arising From the Greek Pursuit of Physical Culture

According to many historians, the medicine ball most people know today originated on or about 300 B.C. It has been suggested that Hippocrates fashioned the first medicine ball out of animal skin and sand. The medicine ball of the time period of the Greeks was used for lifting, carrying, and throwing. As such, it had an integral role in each athlete's physical training regime.

The second piece of modern fitness equipment to arise out of Greek culture was "alteres or halteres." The halteres were crude predecessors of the modern dumbbell. The Greeks used these handheld devices as part of their training in jumping, as well as for swinging movements to build their core and upper-body strength and stamina. Some art work from the Greek period depicts athletes holding oblong weighted objects with handles, which they, in turn, used to perform specific movements, such as lunges, trunk bends and straight-arm raises. According to John Blundell's book entitled, *Muscles and Their Story*, published approximately 1864, the Greek athletes performed exercises to music using these crude dumbbells. These early halteres or dumbbells were made of wax and were often sprinkled with lead to increase their weight. Around the 2nd century AD, the Greek physician Galen in the medical text, *De Sanitate Tuenda*, described the use of weighted implements, called "plummets," that were used to strengthen the body through a series of vigorous movements. These "plummets" were composed of wood, with an iron center. By the 4th century, the halteres or plumments had evolved into a version of today's dumbbell.

A third instrument of training that originated with the Greeks was the stone plate that was lifted overhead by athletes. This plate was simply a flat piece of stone. This tool was one of the earliest attempts at creating an apparatus that could be lifted overhead as a form of resistance training.

It is relatively well established that around 500 A.D., the culture of physical training initially established by the Greeks and espoused by their great philosophers and physicians, began to fade away. Over the next thousand years, exercise and physical training became nearly obsolete.

The Influence of Other Cultures on Fitness

According to the Irish "Book of Leinster," released in the 11th Century A.D., the Celtics introduced sport on or about 1829 B.C. According to oral tradition passed on through the centuries and documented in the book, the first Celtic Games were called the Tailteann Games and were first held in Telltown, County Meath, Ireland in 1829 B.C., continuing till around 554 B.C. According to the "Book of Leinster," some of the events conducted at these games included stone throwing, pole vaulting, geal-ruith (triple jumping) and roth-cleas (the throwing of a wheel-like object for height or distance). This historical claim would indicate that the Celtics originated games prior to the Greeks. Subsequently, the Celtics took the games to Scotland, where later the Border Games and Lakeland Games originated, eventually leading to what we now refer to as the Highland Games. The Highland Games, which are still practiced today, included activities such as the caber toss and the Scottish hammer (written history indicates that the hammer throw was a popular event as far back as the early 1300s during King Edward III's reign). To help competitors prepare for these games, the Celtic

iStockphoto/Thinkstock

The Highland Games, in Scotland, are still practiced today.

and Scottish "athletes" created numerous training regimes to develop strength and stamina (e.g., lifting stones, tossing hammers used in blacksmith shops, etc.) on a year-round basis. Unfortunately, similar to the acrobats of Egypt and the Spartans of Greece, the training protocols used by these Scottish athletes became the privilege of a select few, and never evolved into a form of formal activity that the masses could enjoy or benefit from.

In 1569, nearly one thousand years after the Greek preoccupation with physical training disappeared, an Italian, Hieronymus Mercuialis, published, *"De Arte Gymnastica Aput Ancientes."* In this ground-breaking manuscript, the author described the use of medicine balls and dumbbells as taught by the ancient Greeks. This publication was significant because it represented a focused effort to reintroduce many of the traditional training principles and equipment originated by the Greeks to modern society.

The Advent of Formal Fitness

(The Age of Gymnastics)

Chapter 2

"Yet, it is not strength, so much as health, that is crying want of time. It is stamina, and the power, in each of us, to do our daily work with the least friction and the greatest amount of comfort and ease… Yet, it is health, rather than strength, that is the great requirement of modern man in modern occupations. It is not the power to travel great distances, carry great burdens, lift great weights, or great material obstructions. It is simply that condition of body, and that amount of vital capacity, which shall enable each man in place to pursue his calling, and work in his working life, with the greatest amount of comfort to himself and usefulness to his fellow men."
— Eugen Sandow

The Industrial Revolution and the Fitness Revolution: The Birth and Emergence of Formalized Physical Activity, Equipment, and Facilities

The First Wave of the Fitness Revolution—Formalizing Gymnastics and Calisthenics as Physical Exercise for Human Performance

According to most historians, the Industrial Revolution, or Industrial Evolution as some historians refer to it, had its beginnings in England between 1760 and 1830 (historians sometimes differ on the specific date). The Industrial Revolution rapidly spread from England to other nations in Europe, as well as in the United States. According to some historians, a second wave to the Industrial Revolution occurred around 1850. During this dynamic period in the history of mankind, businesses moved from an agricultural-based to a machine-based economy, and later a technology-driven economy. One of the primary results of this revolution in work dynamics was an environment in which jobs and lifestyles became more sedentary. As the Industrial Revolution grew, a corresponding shift in population demographics occured, as more people moved to cities from the countryside, resulting in the beginning of urbanization. Coinciding with the Industrial Revolution and the resultant urbanization was a revolution in physical culture. This situation involved a shift from sports-based physical culture to physical culture for daily performance.

John Paugh's book represented the beginning of a rebirth, so to speak, of exercise in modern man's daily lifestyle.

During the early part of the industrial revolution (believed to be around 1728), John Paugh published a book, entitled "*A Physiological, Theoretical and Practical Treatise on the Utility of Muscular Exercise for Restoring the Power of Limbs*." In his publication, Paugh described the value of exercise movements with dumbbells. His book represented the beginning of a rebirth, so to speak, of exercise in modern man's daily lifestyle.

Historians often differ on who was the first pioneer to formalize physical culture and bring it to the general public. Many historians of gymnastics, for example, believe that John Basedow of Germany was the first, when he established a school called Philanthropinum in 1774. Basedow's contribution was the endorsement of a philosophy dedicated to the education of the body and mind, accompanied by the creation of a general system designed to support that philosophy. As part of his school's curriculum, students were instructed in what was referred to as "Greek gymnastics", which included exercises, such as running, leaping, wrestling and throwing, that were followed in subsequent years by skating, swimming, and ladder climbing.

In 1793, Johann GutsMuth, often referred to as the grandfather of German physical education, wrote a 700-page book on gymnastic exercises, entitled *Gymnastics for Youth a Practical Guide to Healthful and Amusing Exercise; for the Use of Schools*. Muth's publication featured exercises for young boys and girls. The book, first came out in Germany, and was later published in England in 1800. Finally, in 1802, it was published in the United States. Over the years, GutsMuth's book became the "bible" of German-style gymnastics or physical training. GutsMuth is also credited with creating an early version of the "Weaver Stick," a six-foot long wooden stick that was notched at intervals for adding weights. The Weaver Stick was primarily used for training the forearms, as well as the entire upper body (the Weaver Stick was named after George Weaver of Brooklyn, New York, who popularized its use in the 1940s, approximately 140 years after GutsMuth first developed the instrument).

During the same time period as Basedow and GutsMuth, a third German, Johann Pestalaw, became known as the "founder of free exercise and calisthenics," when in the 1790s he introduced what is referred to by historians of gymnastics as free exercise and calisthenics. In 1799, Franz Nachtegall, a native of Denmark, established what is believed to be the first private gymnastics club and private gym. Nachtegall's private gym offered large-scale group classes, using calisthenics, vaulting, wooden dumbbells and weighted balls. Some individuals believe that Nachtegall may have been the true founder of what is currently referred to as group training or group exercise.

While the aforementioned individuals are viewed as the original pioneers of gymnastics most historians credit Frederick Ludwig Jahn of Germany as the father of modern gymnastics and the developer of Turn, a physical culture club built around gymnastics and the mutual social and patriotic interests of its members. Jahn was the creator of the pommel horse, parallel bars, horizontal bars, vaulting blocks, and the ladder, all of which have become mainstays in facilities of the future. In 1811, Jahn established what is believed to be the first

The Weaver stick

*Rope climbing apparatus
designed by Frederich Jahn*

gymnastics club, Public Turn Platz, which was an open field that offered men and boys mass exercise classes that were designed to help them become physically fit to protect their country. Jahn's initial Turn not only incorporated exercises that employed parallel bars, the pommel horse, and horizontal bars, it also integrated dumbbells and Indian Clubs into structured classes. In 1818, Jahn's first Turn was outlawed by the German government. By 1860, however, over 150 Turns, often called Turnverein, had spread across the globe, offering mass exercise and gymnastics to men and boys. Without question, the evolution of German-style gymnastics owes much of its success to the efforts of Frederich Jahn.

*The first gymnastics club was
established by Frederich Jahn in 1811.*

A Turnverein, a physical culture club offering mass exercise and gymnastics to men and boys, developed by Frederich Jahn.

During the same time period that Frederick Jahn established Turnverein (1811), a Swedish pioneer, Pehr Henrick Ling, frequently referred to as the father of Swedish gymnastics, created Swedish Pedagogic Gymnastics (i.e. Swedish Medical Gymnastics), a systemized approach to gymnastics that was designed to provide specific medical and health benefits. Ling's pedagogic gymnastics was founded on four core principles. The first precept was medical, which was grounded in the belief that exercise, through proper posture and movement, could help overcome or diminish certain ailments of the body. The second underlying factor was military, which focused on the role that exercise plays in developing soldiers who could use either bodily power or weapons to overcome an opponent. Ling's third principle was pedagogical in nature which emphasized the ability of exercise to bring the body under the control of the individual's will (possibly an early example of the mind-body concept). The fourth element in Ling's approach was aesthetic, bodily expression to an individual's internal thoughts and feelings. Ling's medical gymnastics served as the foundation for several styles of medical therapeautic treatment that arose to prominence in the 20th Century, including chiropracty, osteopathy, and Swedish massage. Over time, Ling's medical gymnastics system also became the physical training mainstay of the Swedish military.

Sweden can also lay claim to another pioneer of organized physical activity, Andres Otto Lindfus. In 1803, Lindfus published his doctorial dissertation on an exercise system that was based on the original Greek approach. Lindfus advocated three core principles to training, each of which was similar to the underlying precepts of Ling's form of Swedish gymnastics. Lindfus focused on pedagogical, military, and orthopedic principles, the latter of which, in essence, combined two of Ling's underlying core precepts.

Some historians believe that Ling, along with Frederick Jahn, should be considered equals when discussing the pioneers and "fathers" of systemized exercise for health and fitness. Another important and influential pioneer of physical culture was Captain Phokion Heinrich Clias, an American, who wrote one of the earliest books on gymnastics exercises, entitled *An Elementary Course of Gymnastics Exercises: Intended to Improve the Physical Power of Man*. In reality, who actually is credited with founding formal calisthenics and free exercise, is not as important as being aware of the fact that each of the aforementioned pioneers contributed in his own significant way to establishing the framework that would eventually become the health and fitness facility industry.

> **Another important milestone in the history of physical culture was the creation of a structured approach to exercise for women.**

Another important milestone in the history of physical culture was the creation of a structured approach to exercise for women. In 1827, G.P. Voarino wrote a book entitled, *A Treatise on Calisthenics Exercises Arranged for Private Tuition of Young Ladies.* Two years after Voarino's book was published, Captain Phokion Heinrich Clias published a book that featured his version of exercise for women, entitled *Calisthenics and Exercises for Beauty and Strength for Young Women*. Each of the aforementioned books provided visual and written descriptions of free calisthenics, and accessory-supported calisthenics for women. During this same time period (1824), Catherine Beecher opened the Hartford Female Seminary, based in Hartford, Connecticut, where she introduced American-style gymnastics for women. Beecher's underlying vision was for women to find happiness by living "good," which involved a balanced lifestyle that included healthy eating and exercise. In 1856 Catherine Beecher authored a book, entitled *Physiology and Calisthenics for Schools and Families,* which espoused her ideas regarding exercise for women. In 1873 she authored another landmark book, entitled *Housekeeper and Healthkeeper*, which set forth in greater detail her approach to proper nutrition and exercise for women. She is credited with developing American-style gymnastics and calisthenics for women.

Another significant milestone in the advancement of fitness training during the later part of the 1800s involved Dudley Allen Sargent, (the director of the Hemenway Gymnasium and an assistant professor of physical education at Harvard), who developed a codified system of fitness testing to help personalize exercise regimes. He was a pioneer in the use of anthropometric measurements and dynamometry (i.e., the measurement of muscular strength). His pioneering efforts involved identifying the physical needs of individuals, and then using this data to design personalized fitness regimes (he conducted over 10,000 assessments). In his efforts to accurately measure the physical attribues of his subjects, Sargent utilized several types of dynamometers. He is credited as being the "grandfather of fitness testing" and a pioneer in the practice of combining physical measurements with personalized exercise routines that employed progressive resistance exercise machines. In fact, he is credited with designing the first progressive resistance pulley machines.

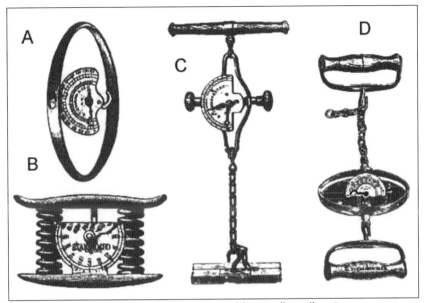

Examples of dynamometers used by Dudley Allen Sargent

The Establishment of Clubs and Facilities for Practicing Calisthenics and Gymnastics

As indicated previously, the first gymnastics club, Turnverein, was established in 1811. By the 1850s, the number of such clubs had grown to over 150. In fact, during the latter half of the nineteenth century, particularly from 1840 to 1900, gymnastics clubs and free exercise really began to take hold in both Europe and the U.S.

One of the earliest of these clubs in Europe opened in Brussels in 1848, which one year later, in 1849, was then moved to Paris France. The 9500 meter club, called "GymnaseTriat", was created by Hippolyte Triat. Gymnase Triat was dedicated to serving every aspect of physical training, and included every modern piece of equipment available at the time, including ropes, pommel horses, horizontal bars, Indian clubs, dumbbells, and globe barbells.

Triat's barbells are believed to be among the first barbells (called Bares A spheres De 6 Kilos) ever offered for use to the public. These barbells were long bars with 6-kilo globe weights attached to their ends. Triat was also the first club operator to sell shares in his facility (he sold 250,000 shares at five francs each, raising over one million francs in the process) to obtain the funds necessary to develop and operate his facility. The individuals who purchased shares in his gym could then redeem their shares for private lessons or for payment of the membership fees.

Hippolyte Triat

Bill Pearl Enterprises

Hippolyte Triat's gymnasium club (circa 1840s)

Around the same time as Triat opened his club in Paris, America was getting its first club, the Boston YMCA, which opened in 1850. This facility is considered by many individuals to be the first American Club, while other historians give that credit to Turnvereins, which first opened a club in 1848 in Cincinnati, Ohio, and one year later, opened a second facility in St. Louis, Missouri. The first Turnverein, as well as the Boston YMCA, had fully equipped gyms that featured rings, ropes, pommel horse, benches, wooden dumbbells, Swedish ladders, and combat art areas.

The Boston YMCA in the 1850s

Exercise class in a Sokol athletic club

Shortly after the appearance of the Turnverein in Cincinnati, and the Boston YMCA, two athletic clubs, still operating today, the Olympic Club of San Francisco and the New York Athletic Club of New York, which opened in 1860 and 1868, respectfully. These two landmark facilities integrated the emerging practice of physical culture for men with the need to provide a social arena in which individuals of common interest could gather together. During the same decade that the Olympic Club of San Francisco and the New York Athletic Club opened, immigrants from the Czech Republic established a series of gymnastic clubs in St. Louis (1865) and New York (1867) called Sokol. These facilities were similar to the Turnverein clubs that were established by German immigrants, in that they offered structured group calisthenics and gymnastics, along with a strong social element. The Sokols and the Turnvereins represented the first two large-scale introductions of social athletic clubs.

The pool in the New York Athletic Club in the 1800s.

The First Hundred Years: A Portrait of the NYAC

During the fifty-year period from 1850 to 1900, a number of prominent athletic clubs and gymnasiums opened around the world. A list of these noteworthy facilities includes the New Orleans Athletic Club, New Orleans, LA (1872); the Detroit Athletic Club, Detroit, Michigan (1887); the Hemenway Gymnasium, Boston, Massachusetts (1888) ; The Lille Athletic Club, Lille, France which was operated by Professor Edmond Desbonnet (1885), the Vienna Athletic Club, Vienna, Austria (1880s), the Wrestling and Weightlifting Club of Saint Petersburg, Saint Petersburg, Russia (1885); the Athletic Club of Florence, Florence, Italy (1880s); the Chicago Athletic Association Facility, Chicago, Illinois (1893); and the London YMCA, London, England (1888). These facilities had several underlying principles in common, including the fact that they catered to men and had a focus on sports and physical culture. These athletic facilities also had gymnastic areas that featured gymnastic-style equipment, barbells, dumbbells, medicine balls, ring bells, Indian clubs, ladders, rings, horizontal bars, etc. In addition, these facilities provided a setting where group calisthenics could be conducted, as well as offered a social element to their members, based on bringing men of like interests together.

In the early 1890s, Professor Attila (i.e., Louis Durlacher) moved from England, where he had operated a gym for the great strongmen and dignataries of Europe, to the United States. Once he settled in the U.S., he established his "Studio and School of Physical Culture" in 1894. Attila's studio went on to become the most popular "gym" in the U.S. during the 1890s and early 1900s, serving as the gym of choice for athletes, as well as for the rich and famous of the period. It represented the first modern style gym in the United States and would set the framework for other gyms that would open after the turn of the century.

Bill Pearl Enterprises

The Lille Athletic Club in Lille, France,
founded by Edmond Desbonnet in 1885.

The London YMCA in the late 1800s.

A Different Type of Club Arises That Plays a Role in the Future of the Industry

During the 1860s, a different type of club, one not dedicated to gymnastics or calisthenics, arose in Europe and the United States. These different clubs were referred to as tennis and racquet clubs. The first "tennis or racquet club" of record is Hampton Court, which opened in 1625 and offered "court tennis", the precursor to lawn tennis or modern tennis. The first actual modern tennis club, the All England Lawn Tennis and Croquet Club (now known as Wimbledon), was founded in 1868. The first tennis championships, now known as the Wimbledon Championships, were held in 1877. During the next decade, tennis clubs began to prosper. In 1876, the first tennis court club was established in Boston, MA with a court on Buckingham Street. In 1877, the Dublin Lawn Tennis Club opened (now the Fitzwilliam Lawn Tennis Club). In 1880, the Newport Casino in Rhode Island was formed (now home to the Tennis Hall of Fame) and became the second tennis club in the United States. Shortly thereafter, in 1886, the New York Tennis Club was built.

While tennis clubs did not intertwine with the original athletic clubs and gymnastics clubs of the 19th century, nearly a century later, they would become a driving force in the health and fitness facility industry, and a founding element of the International Racquet and Sports Association (IRSA).

Equipment Innovations of the 18th and 19th Century

One of the distinguishing characteristics of this new era of physical culture was the development of innovative apparatus and equipment to enhance the productivity of physical culture training. As such, during the early part of the 19th century, gymnastics apparatus become the most popular form of training apparatus. Frederick Jahn is credited with inventing the pommel horse, parallel bars, horizontal bars, vaulting box, and ladder (an implement that is commonly referred to as the Swedish ladder). These early gymnastics devices, along with wooden dumbbells and ropes, became a mainstay in the training toolbox of physical culturists.

One of the earliest pieces of modern fitness equipment to be developed was the wooden dumbbell. According to historical records, the actual precursor to the dumbbell, the halteres, was created by the Greeks in 3000 BC. In turn, the modern dumbbell had its origins with the wooden dumbbell, which was first used extensively in the early 1700s. Ben Franklin, for example, was known to have exercised regularly with wooden dumbbells. In a letter written around 1772, Franklin shared his enthusiasm for training with the dumbbell, when he wrote:

> *"By the use of it, I have in forty swings, quickened
> my pulse from sixty to one hundred beats a minute
> counted by a second watch, and I suppose the
> warmth generally increases with quickness of pulse."*

Most historians of fitness trace the development of kettlebells to Russia, where references to them first appeared in 1704.

In time, toward the middle of the 1800s, the dumbbell became an extremely popular training tool. In 1865, an exercise enthusiast, George Barker Windship of Boston, MA, created the first plate-loaded dumbbells, which ranged in weight from eight pounds to 101 pounds.

A second equipment innovation to occur during approximately this same time period was the development of the kettlebell. Most historians of fitness trace the development of kettlebells to Russia, where references to them first appeared in 1704. Russians referred to those who trained with kettlebells as "gireviks," given that "girya" is the Russian word for a kettlebell. According to Russian lore, gireviks competed in villages for the honor of being the strongest man or "Bogatirs."

A third innovation that transpired during this time period was the "wand," an early version of the barbell. The wand was a weighted wooden stick, similar to the body bar. Mention of the wand and its use appeared in Nicholas Andry's book that was published in 1743, entitled *Orthopedia*. Iron wands were used in many Turnvereins starting in the 1850s, usually in the form of group-exercise activities (an image of an early form of a Body Pump class would seem to be appropriate).

The fourth innovation to appear during this period was the barbell, which evolved from the iron-weighted wand. The first barbells were believed to be shot-loaded globes that were attached to each end of a weighted bar. Some individuals credit Hippolyte Triat with originating the barbell, while others point to George Barker Windship, who introduced shot-loaded globe barbells in 1865.

Indian clubs were also added to the toolbox of many physical culturists during the early part of the 18th century. Indian clubs, initially developed in India as a weapon, later became a training device for Indian soldiers. When the British colonized India, they adopted many of the training protocols used in India, including the use of Indian clubs. Donald Walker, author of *British Manly Exercise*, published in 1834, introduced Indian club exercise to England. Thirty years later, in 1866, Sim Kehoe wrote a landmark book, entitled *Indian Club Exercises*, that formally introduced this particular type of equipment into the training lexicon of physical culturists throughout the world, including America.

The first strength training machine was developed by Captain James Chiosso, a gymnastics professor at London University College. His device, called the Polymachinon, a multifaceted training apparatus that used numerous pulleys and related devices. Chiosso's machine, in many ways, resembled the multi-station functional trainers that are currently popular in many health/fitness clubs. The Polymachinon is an example of a piece of equipment that was ahead of its time, and, as a consequence, never caught on with the general public.

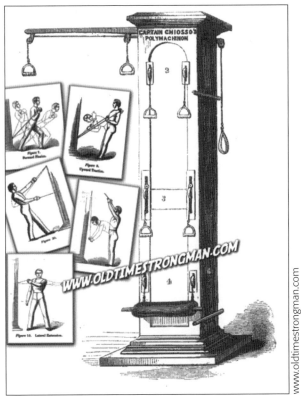

*The Polymachinon machine,
developed by James Chiosso*

A ring bell weight

As physical training programs progressed over the latter half of the 19th century, physical culturists and strongmen looked for new tools to apply their trade. During this same time frame, kettlebells, medicine balls, Indian clubs, dumbbells, barbells and ring bells became popular strength training devices. Ring bells were actually a knock-off of a weighted device that live performance theaters used to tie down curtains during performances. The ring bells allowed oldtime strongmen to perform a variety of weighted resistance movements, similar to those performed with kettlebells. Another weighted device that became popular during the latter half of the 19th century was the block weight, a solid weighted object, with a small handle, that could be used to performing a variety of strongman movements. Another piece of resistance training equipment that evolved in the late 1800s was the "captain's wheel", a device designed to assist in the development of upper-body muscles used in rotary-type movements. Finally, strand-pulling equipment (e.g., chest expanders and related strand-designed devices) were also extremely popular in the late 1800s.

The introduction of barbells as tools for resistance training occurred during the middle part of the 19th century. At the time, most barbells were custom made by specialty manufacturers. Early strongmen often called barbells "two-handed dumbbells." In the 1890s, Charles Heap and Company of London

NAUTICAL WHEEL

An adaptation of the steering wheel of a vessel. The friction brake, that forms the resistance, is simple and durable. The arms or spokes are supported by the rim. The machine presents a fine appearance, the arms being ash, and the mountings Japan finish.

No. 320 NAUTICAL WHEEL, frictional, 48 inches diameter, . .

Weight 100 lbs. Packed for Shipment

To set up, secure strongly to the wall about four feet from the floor to the centre.

A captain's wheel

became one of the first manufacturers of weight training equipment, producing most of the equipment used by Eugen Sandow and his peers.

Dudley Allen Sargent, an assistant professor of physical education at Harvard and the director of the Hemenway Gymnasium at Harvard from 1879 to 1919, is credited by most individuals with developing variable-resistance pulley systems. Beginning in the early 1880s, Sargent designed a variety of pulley systems, using stacks of weighted plates that allowed exercisers to adjust the weight to their specific physical limitations. Among the pulley systems that he developed were an abdominal pulley system, a chest pulley system, and back pulley system. Sargent was also the first person to introduce free-standing equipment that required users to position themselves in the equipment in either a seated or standing position. At one time, he had 56 of these machines in the Hemenway Gymnasium.

One of the pulleys developed by Dudley Allen Sargent

An exerciser working out on the Sargent inomotor machine

The Sargent pulley system in the early 1900s in New York City

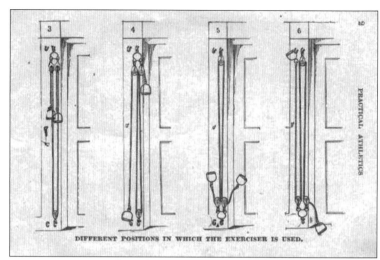

The Whitely Exerciser machine

Alexey Whitely was one of the first entrepreneurs to incorporate pulley training in his consumer-oriented exercise regimens. In 1894, Whitely introduced the Whitely Exerciser, a single-pulley device that was designed to be set-up in the home or gym and was supported by a complete exercise system that would allow trainees to obtain a full-body workout in 30 minutes (not all that unlike suspension training of the 21st century). During the late 1880s and 1890s, pulley devices, both single-and double-wall mounted, evolved into an important piece of training equipment for many physical culturists, especially those individuals who were involved in developmental activities involving muscular endurance. One of the most unusual pulley devices to emerge during this time period was the Spalding Semi-circle Strength Developer, which was developed by Dudley Allen Sargent and resembled a half-moon bench, with pulleys. Spalding was one of several firms that manufactured equipment, such as this particular device for the small cadre of gyms that operated during the late 1800s and early 1900s.

The Spaulding semi-circle strength developer machine, which was originally known as the Dudley Sargent Chest Machine

Resistance training equipment tended to be the predominant choice of equipment in the early 1800s, while cardiovascular equipment for the gym evolved in later decades. The first piece of indoor cardiovascular equipment to emerge was a rowing machine developed in 1871 by William B. Curtis, a founding member of the New York Athletic Club. Curtis's rowing machine involved the use of a flywheel and ratchet system, and was patented shortly after its creation. Curtis's rowing machine became a template for future rowing machines. During the early 20th century, rowing machines were the most popular piece of cardiovascular equipment in athletic clubs and gyms.

In 1875, the first treadmill was developed—the Level Power treadmill. The Level Power treadmill was not designed as a treadmill for human performance, but rather as a device that would allow small and large animals to run on it in order to generate power for farming machinery (e.g., butter churns, threshing machines, etc.). For example Nicholas Potter was awarded three patents for treadmills manufactured in Troy, Pa, collectively known as the "Enterprise Dog Power." His first patent, issued in February 28, 1871, covered the adjustable pivoting track frame. In September 21, 1875, he received a patent that addressed the method of tightening the track and a windlass for elevating the track. This particular treadmill used a roller track, rather than the usual leather belt. Potter's third patent, issued in June 28, 1881, detailed an adjustable

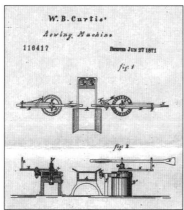

The rowing machine that was developed by William B. Curtis in 1871

www.rowinghistory.net

William B. Curtis (dark suit) and members of the New York Athletic Club

*The Level
Power treadmill*

Frank O'Rourke

and easily removable track frame, a feature that provided an advantage when repairs need to be made to the treadmill. Potter's final design is typical of most surviving Enterprise treadmills.

In the 1850s, a Swedish physician and follower of Pehr Henrick Ling's Medical Gymnastics, Gustav Zander, experimented with a new approach to medical gymnastics. Zander felt that the form of exercise promoted by Ling, while effective, could be adapted and could be made to have a greater impact on individuals who were seeking to enhance their muscular development, both from a preventative and a rehabilitative perspective. Zander's experimentation lead him to the development of progressive exertion "resistance machines," employing springs, graduated levers, weights, and pulleys. By 1865, he had created 27 different mechanical machines, each based on creating resistance that could be adapted to the specific needs of a particular individual. Zander introduced his machines to the medical community and public when he opened his Medico-Mechanical Institute in Sweden in 1865. Zander would later open institutes in London, England and New York, New York during the 1880s and 1890s, both of which made use of his machines. For a period of time during those two decades, Zander's machines were also used in the field of industrial medicine for rehabilitative medical therapy. During the early 1900s, the Homested Resort in Hot Springs, Virgina installed 36 Zander machines to complement their hot spring therapies. By the 1930s, Zander's machines virtually disappeared, as a result not only of his death, but also the impact of the Depression.

*The pulldown machine
created by Gustav Zander*

*Individuals performing calisthenic exercises with dumbbells, as shown
in James Watson's book,* Handbook of Calisthenics and Gymnastics:
A Complete Drill Book for Schools, Families and Gymnasiums

Books and Literature on Fitness Abound

One of the most widely read books of this time period was *Indian Club
Exercises*, which was authored by Sim D. Kehoe in 1866. What began in 1862
as a passion became the basis for a comprehensive book on how to perform
exercises with Indian clubs of various sizes. As such, Indian club exercise
routines became a staple of the U.S. Army, as well as for early baseball clubs
and for the crew teams from Harvard and Yale. One year later, in 1867, Dio
Lewis published a book entitled, *The New Gymnastics*,
which offered formalized instruction in calisthenics.
In 1873, Catherine Beecher, who founded American
Style Gymnastics for Women in 1823, authored a
book, entitled *Housekeeper and Health Keeper*,
published by Harper & Brothers of New York. In her
book, she laid out guidance for proper dieting and
physical exercise for women. One year later, Beecher
wrote another book, *Educational Reminiscences and
Suggestions*, which was published by J.B. Ford of New
York. In that book, Beecher wrote:

Catherine Beecher

*"When physical education takes the proper place
in our schools, young girls will be trained in the
classrooms to move head, hand, and arms gracefully,
to sit, stand, and walk properly and to pursue
calisthenics exercises for physical development as a
regular school duty as much as their studies."*

*The author of one of the most
read books of the 19th century on
exercise was Eugen Sandow, shown
above with an array of workout tools*

In 1882, James Madison Watson authored, *Handbook of Calisthenics and Gymnastics: A Complete Drill Book for Schools, Families and Gymnasiums*, published by E. Stieger & Company of New York. In his comprehensive book, Watson laid out a complete series of calisthenics, that could be performed with and without the use of dumbbells and accessories. Watson's book featured a number of calisthenics routines. Interestingly, many of the calisthenics exercise routines detailed by Watson in his book were taught in a group setting to music, which was performed by live musicians. Over the next two decades, numerous physical educators and physical culture specialists wrote their own treatises on exercise. In the late 1890s, one of the most read books of the 19th century was *Sandow's System of Physical Training*, written by Eugen Sandow and edited by G. Mercer Adams. The book, which was published in 1894 by Gale & Polden Ltd of London, England, set forth Sandow's unique and inspiring program of physical training, that employed dumbbells, barbells, chest expanders, and free-hand calisthenics. In 1891, Alex Whitely penned a revolutionary book, entitled *The Shortest Route and Fastest Time to Health and Strength or Practical Athletics for Busy People*. In his book, published by the Continental Printing Company of St. Louis, Whitely introduced the world to the "30-Minute Workout," that featured the use of his new invention, the Whitely Exerciser. In the introduction to his book, Whitely outlined the essence of his philosophy when he stated:

*"The problem seems to be how to obtain
exercise without expending time or energy…
the strictly American style of the shortest route
and fastest time to health and fitness."*

The Age of Muscle
(The First Half of the 20th Century)

Chapter 3

"Now apart from extraordinary causes, there is absolutely no reason why any man should ever be ill, as long as he keeps his body so physically fit as to safeguard it against any breakdown… fifteen or twenty minutes daily exercise will be all-sufficient for this purpose. Surely no very heavy price to pay for such a valuable result."

— George Hackenschmidt
From his book,
The Way to Live in Health & Physical Fitness,
published in 1935

The First 50 Years—Consumerism, Materialism, Depression, and War Influence the Practice of Fitness

The period from 1900 to 1945 was marked by two World Wars, the Great Depression, and the rapid development of new technology and communications. During this period, Americans began to make inroads into the global economy and culture. Starting in the early 1900s and continuing over the next four to five decades, consumerism, materialism, inflation, vaudeville, and advancing technologies, as well as two World Wars and a great depression, shaped the world. In doing so, these factors also influenced the evolution of the fitness industry. During this span, fitness began to emerge as part of modern society, moving from the exclusive domain of fanatical physical culturists to the realm of the average citizen. From 1900 until the onset of the Great War, the business of physical culture, or fitness, was heavily influenced by the great physical culturists of the late 19th century and their disciples who took the lead in this undertaking during the early part of the 20th century.

Physical culture during the first four decades of the 20th century revolved around strength training and its related offshoots.

The Early Artisans and Influencers of Fitness at the Beginning of the 20th Century

Physical culture during the first four decades of the 20th century revolved around strength training and its related offshoots, including circus performances and vaudeville acts that often focused on unusual feats of strength, balance, and physical culture. As such, such notable individuals as Eugen Sandow, Professor Louis Attila, George Hackenshmidt, Alan Calvert, Earle Liederman, Sig Klein, Warren Lincoln Travis, and Charles Atlas, among others, became the innovators and promoters of the fitness industry. It is interesting to note that each of these legendary individuals engaged at one time or another in the performing arts, in particular live stage acts (e.g., circus, vaudeville, etc.). These people, including Sandow, Atlas, Klein, and Liederman, all demonstrated their physiques and strengths on stage, and in the case of Atlas and Sandow, made significant money doing so. Sandow was documented as having earned as much as $3,500 weekly ($75,000 in 2011 dollars) for eight shows. In fact, during his lifetime, he netted well over $1 million (an amount equivalent to over $21.5 million in 2011 dollars) from his exhibitions and tours.

One of the most influential and possibly controversial fitness pioneers of the early 20th century was Bernarr Macfadden (his original name was Bernard McFadden). He is often called the father of physical culture. Macfadden first came to prominence in the 1890s, taking the world stage at about the same time as Eugen Sandow. Macfadden opened his first studio in 1887, marketing himself as a "kinestherapist" (the first person to coin this phrase) and a teacher of higher physical culture. In 1894, he created the Macfadden exerciser. By 1899, he had opened a series of physical culture clubs. In 1899, he published his first issue of *Physical Culture*, a magazine dedicated to the pursuit of physical culture and health, a publication that by 1903 had circulation of over 100,000. The magazine ran for 50 years, and had the longest circulation run of any health and fitness magazine in U.S. history. He also published *Beauty and Health for Women*. During the late 1800s and early 1900s, Macfadden toured the country, often with his family, promoting his brand of physical culture, while also serving as the first "global advocate" of physical culture, training, and healthy eating. Macfadden's influence endured well into the 20th century, with the publication of the first edition of *Macfadden's Encyclopedia of Physical Culture* in 1911, a publication that had seven separate editions. By the third edition, the encyclopedia, which began as one volume, had evolved into eight volumes, that covered an array of topics ranging from anatomy and physiology to the diagnosis and treatment of disease. Macfadden also established the Macfadden Healthatorium, first in Battlecreek, Michigan and later in Chicago, Illinois. The Healthatorium was a school for educating aspiring physical culturists in alternative health practices. He also established the Bernarr Macfadden Institute, a school for training professionals in physcultopathy. In the early 1900s, Macfadden was involved in a short-lived experiment, called Physical Culture City—a town built in New Jersey that was dedicated to healthy living. One particular quote that appeared in a 1906 issue of his *Physical Culture Magazine* speaks to Macfadden's vision for the future of fitness, as well as to his passion and contributions to spreading the gospel of fitness during the late 19th and early 20th centuries:

> *"When the importance of physical culture is recognized, when men and women realize its true importance, it will enter into every phase of human life. There is hardly a question in life which physical culture should not be a part."*

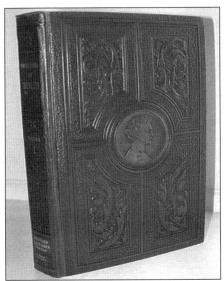

One volume of Bernarr Macfadden's Encyclopedia of Physical Culture

An ad that appeared in the early 1900s for Alan Calvert's barbells

In 1902, Alan Calvert established the Milo Barbell Company, the first company to mass-produce barbells, dumbbells, globe bells, and kettlebells. In conjunction with forming the first manufacturing company dedicated to fitness equipment, Calvert wrote and distributed mail-order courses in weight training that introduced the public to the core principles of exercise overload and exercise progressions. In 1911, Calvert authored the first comprehensive book on weightlifting entitled, *The Truth about Weightlifting*. In fact, Calvert's efforts to generate a series of mail-order courses and books on strength training were quite successful. In 1914, his training booklets became a bi-monthly publication called *Strength Magazine*. In 1903, a manufacturing company in Rhode Island, the Narragansett Machine Company, began producing gymnastic equipment on a mass level. By 1910, the company was also manufacturing barbell sets and fitness accessory equipment, such as pulley systems, Roman chairs, ladders, etc. In the process, these two companies became the first two equipment vendors to influence the development of gyms. Approximately two decades later, a third influential fitness vendor was established—York Barbell Company.

From 1900 to 1945, a proliferation occurred in the number of books, magazines, and mail-order courses on how to train that were on the market. During the second and third decades of this century, mail-order courses in physical culture became extremely popular, with advertisements appearing in nearly all of the popular physical-culture publications. The two most successful entrepreneurs in the mail-order business were Earle Liederman and Charles Atlas. Earle Liederman's mail order business became so expansive (i.e., employing approximately 300 employees, with a weekly advertising bill of $25,000) that by the middle of the 1920s, the postal service opened a branch office in his mid-town Manhattan office. The various mail-order publications promoted a variety of training protocols, each of which guaranteed success. The most popular form of training promoted in the literature was weightlifting exercises that employed barbells, dumbbells, expanders, and muscle-control techniques.

Concurrent with the growth in publications promoting the use of barbells and dumbbells was the introduction of exercise programs based on muscle control, an approach that was subsequently later coined as "dynamic tension" by Charles Atlas. Another type of muscle control training (e.g., muscle flexing, isometric training, etc.) was introduced in 1904 by Professor Edward Ittman in his book, *Physical Culture by Means of Muscular Resistance and Breathing*. Only five years later, Maxalding, a program similar to the resistance training protocol promoted by Ittman (e.g., muscle control), subsequently became hugely successful, selling to a worldwide audience until the 1970s. The Maxalding program was developed by two legendary strongmen, Max Sick (e.g., Maxick) and Monte Saldo. Twenty years after the introduction of control training and isometrics, yet another approach to training, "dynamic tension," was introduced and promoted by Charles Atlas. A third form of strength training, expander or strand training, was also prominently promoted in the literature of this era. Expander training involved the use of devices that had handles and strands made of either rubber or steel springs. Many of the strongmen of this era, including Eugen Sandow, incorporated strand training. Alfred Danks was one of the most pre-eminent proponents of expander training for muscular development and strength. In addition to Danks, another avid proponent of this form of training was Roy H. Noe of Memphis, Tennessee, a noted exercise professional at the time.

An ad featuring Charles Atlas that appeared in 1932

A sample listing of the books and mail-order courses that were produced during this four-decade period includes the following:

- *Milo Bodybuilding and Muscle Developing Exercises* by Alan Calvert (1911)
- *Milo Barbell Courses* (one, two and three) by Alan Calvert (1924)
- *Muscle Flexing* by Antone Matysek (1921)
- *Professor Attila's Five Pound Dumb-bell Exercises* by Professor Louis Attila (1913)
- *Maxalding: Nature's Way for Mental and Physical Fitness* by Antone-Saldo (1930)
- *Gospel of Strength According to Sandow* by Eugen Sandow (1904)
- *The Way to Live in Health and Fitness* by George Hackenschmidt (1934)
- *Macfadden's Encyclopedia of Physical Culture* by Bernarr Macfadden (1911, first edition)
- *Danks System of Physical Culture* by Alfred Danks (early 1900s)
- *Physical Culture* by J.J. Miller (1908)
- *Muscle Control and Barbell Exercises* by Ghosh and Sen Gupta (1930)
- *Muscle Building by Earle Liederman* by Earle Liederman (1924)
- *Muscle Building and Physical Culture* by George Jowett (1927)

Muscle Building by Earle Liederman

EXERCISE FOR THE CHEST AND ARMS
Push up and down from the floor, keeping the body stiff. This exercise can be made more difficult by elevating the feet as shown in the above photograph. (See chapter on the chest.)
106

Earle Liederman performing a muscle-building pushup

Accompanying this growth in books and mail-order programs was the development of several magazines and newsletters that were dedicated to the pursuit of physical fitness. In 1899, the Macfadden Publishing Company introduced *Physical Culture Magazine*, an undertaking that remained in circulation for approximately 50 years (the longest running fitness publication in American history). A few years later, Macfadden Publishing introduced *Beauty and Health for Women*, and in 1924, released *Muscle Builder Magazine*. One year prior to the publication of *Physical Culture Magazine* in the United States, *Health & Strength Magazine* (1898), was published in England, a magazine that is still in publication today, making it the longest running fitness publication of all time. In 1905, Eugen Sandow published *Sandow's Magazine*, one of the most popular magazines at the time. In 1931 and continuing to 1933, the *Klein Bell*, a relatively small newsletter publication written by Sig Klein was published. The *Klein Bell* provided tips on training and nutrition. In 1932, Bob Hoffman, established *Strength and Health Magazine* as part of his empire of weight training and physical culture, an enterprise that included both the York Barbell Company and the York Barbell Club and Gym.

One of the more unique "fitness" publications for educating the public about exercise was produced in England during the early 1900s. In 1914, Will's Cigarette Company produced Will's Cigarette Cards, a series of two-sided cards that included descriptions and depictions of calisthenics and related exercises. One side of the card had a picture of an exercise, while the other side contained a description of how to perform the exercise. These cards were placed inside the packages of cigarettes that were offered for sale by the company. As a result, these cards were distributed to a relatively large audience of men who typically did not exercise. In addition to Will's Cigarette Cards, Eugen Sandow also produced a series of cigarette cards during the early 20th century.

Fitness was not immune to the evolving level of consumerism and materialism of the early 20th century.

In reality, fitness was not immune to the evolving level of consumerism and materialism of the early 20th century. During this period, the number of mail-order courses and correspondence schools offering physical-culture programs that guaranteed transformations in the appearance and strength of the end user proliferated. Eugen Sandow and Bernarr Macfadden opened their Institutes of Physical Culture in the late 1800s and early 1900s, both of which offered mail-order courses and certificates in physical culture. In the 1920s, George Jowett established the "Jowett Institute of Physical Culture," which became one of the most popular institutes or mail-order courses of physical culture during 20s. Lionel Strongfort, another early strongman, established the Institute of Physical Culture, which in the 1930s proclaimed itself to be the "World's Foremost Physical Culture and Health Correspondence School."

Earle Liederman started his mail-order courses in the 20s. At one time, Liederman had over 300 employees to respond to the demand for his courses. Prior to the Great Depression, Liderman's mail-order business was the largest in the industry, as well as the most profitable. Between 1910 and 1920, his 12-week home course sold for $28, a price that rose by the middle of the roaring 20s to $47. One of Liederman's famous quotes that appeared in advertisements for his mail-order courses detailed his underlying philosophy regarding the value of resistance exercise, as follows:

"If you have a wart on your nose, you would
worry yourself sick…you would pay most any price
to get rid of it. Wake up! Come to your senses!
Everyone despises the weakling."

As consumerism and materialism peaked from 1900 to 1930 (1929 saw the collapse of a number of these mail-order enterprises), many of the era's great strongmen and physical culture specialists reached out to the average citizen through mail-order courses that promised "physical miracles" if these individuals adopted the recommended exercise regimes. Macfadden, Sandow, Strongfort, Klein, Liederman, and Calvert, among numerous others, promoted their programs as the "best" by placing advertisements in various books, magazines, and papers. While all these health advocates experienced some degree of success in promoting their courses, with Sandow being the most successful during the first two decades, it was Earle Liederman in the 20s and subsequently Charles Atlas in the 30s who took mail-order fitness training to the next level.

The cover of the October 1938
issue of Physical Culture *magazine*

A Memorable Mail-Order Pioneer

Charles Atlas, born Angelo Siciiano in New York, was a protégé of Bernarr Macfadden. Early on in his career, Charles Atlas was a model who earned upwards of $100 a week. In fact, Charles Atlas was one of the most sought after male models of the era, known for having an incredible physique. Atlas claimed to have developed his extraordinary physique with muscle control and isometrics (truth be known, some interested bystanders also claim that he was also an avid user of barbell and dumbbell exercises). In 1921, and again in 1922, Charles Atlas entered Bernarr Macfadden's "World's Most Perfectly Developed Man Competition." This competition, sponsored by Macfadden, was initially intended to help promote Macfadden's ideal of the perfectly built man, as well as to help sell his magazines and other publications to the public. In 1921, and again in 1922, Charles Atlas won, in one instance beating over 775 competitors for the title of "World's Most Perfectly Developed Man." After his second victory, Bernarr Macfadden, sensing a great talent, took Charles Atlas under his tutelage. He subsequently introduced Atlas to Dr. Frederick Tilney, a homeopathic physician and physical culturist. Together, Tilney and Atlas wrote a training course (featuring muscle control and isometric opposition exercises, with a few range-of-motion exercises) that encompassed both 12 initial lessons and a thirteenth lasting lesson. The course was promoted through Macfadden's magazines, and later in newspapers, magazines, books, and comic books. By 1929, the three individuals had incorporated as Charles Atlas, Ltd, a mail-order and in-home exercise course company.

One of the most successful mail-order and in-home exercise companies in the early twentieth ccentury featured Charles Atlas.

The business initially floundered, and Charles Atlas ended up as the sole proprietor. Shortly after taking over the business, he met Charles Roman, a recent marketing and business graduate from New York University. Roman was the right person at the right time. He added marketing muscle and innovation to a business model that was stagnating. Roman coined the phrase "dynamic tension," and created the themes for all future advertisements that promoted the course, including: "Hey Skinny" and "97-Pound Weakling." Concurrently, Roman began placing ads in comic books, which at the time (the period of the Great Depression) were incredibly popular among young men. It was the unique blend of Charles Atlas's persona and personal selling skills, Roman's incredible marketing savvy, and possibly the circumstances of the Great Depression that took Charles Atlas to the pinnacle of mail-order fitness courses (it should be noted that his courses are still available today).

Charles Atlas saw physical exercise as a means for men to gain self confidence (he promoted physical size as a means of gaining self-confidence during a period in history when many men lost self-confidence). What set him apart most and created a legacy that still stands today, both as a legend of physical culture and business, was his unique ability to personalize his program for everyone. Charles wrote letters to all his students, creating what he believed, and the students felt, was an intimate bond between teacher and student. *Forbes Magazine* called Atlas a "super salesman." His millions of students, however, saw him as their teacher, coach, and personal guide to physical perfection.

Equipment Innovations and Manufacturers of the First 50 Years

At the turn of the century, equipment had become an integral part of training for most practitioners of physical culture, and a pivotal fixture in athletic clubs and gyms of the period. During the first two decades of the 20th century, most of the equipment used in athletic clubs and gyms resembled the original devices developed by the pioneers of the late 18th century (e.g., kettlebells, wooden dumbbells, barbells, pulleys, rowing machines, strand pullers, etc.).

During the early part of the 20th century, Professor Attila (Louis Durlacher) developed the Roman column and the Roman chair. The Roman column was a column or pole on which a person would hang upside down and then proceed to perform a form of sit-up or trunk curl that strengthened the abdominal area and hip flexors. The Roman chair was a bench that allowed the user to perform a similar type of movement. A student of Professor Attila's, Sig Klein, is credited with developing the first leg press machine by attaching a chain and platform to the wall and then adding free weight plates to the platform.

A number of unique pieces of fitness equipment originated during the first two decades of the 20th century. Eugen Sandow was responsible for developing several of these items, including Sandow's Physical Training Machine, Sandow's Pushup Machine, and Sandow's Developer. The Sandow Physical Training Leg Machine was a unique machine that used strands to create resistance that allowed a user's legs to be trained with various movements, including flexion, extension, and abduction. Sandow's Pushup Machine, similar to his Leg Training

At the turn of the century, equipment had become an integral part of training for most practitioners of physical culture, and a pivotal fixture in athletic clubs and gyms of the period.

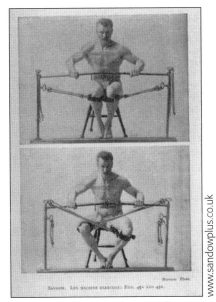

Eugen Sandow's leg machine

Eugen Sandow's pushup machine

Gustav Zander's torso resistance machine (1903)

Gustav Zander's leg extension machine (1903)

Machine, used strands to create resistance. Sandow's third piece of equipment, Sandow's "Developer," resembled the pulley devices of the time, employing strands, instead of cables and weights, to create resistance. Sandow was an avid user and promoter of these pieces of equipment, and included them in many of his training courses.

Another unique training device, the Schmidt Machine or Schmidt Automatic Exerciser was also developed in the early part of the century by Professor Adrian Schmidt. The Schmidt Machine was one of the first commercial pieces of strength equipment to gain widespread use. The machine involved the use of leverage to create resistance, thereby reducing the need for extensive weights.

In the late 1880s, Dudley Allen Sargent began developing pulley systems and free-standing exercise machines. By the beginning of the 20th century, Sargent had developed over 30 distinct machines for training the various areas of the body, including calf machines, chest machines, leg machines, etc.

The Kern's & Laflin Rowing Machine evolved from the original Curtis rowing machine that was developed in 1871. Efforts to distribute this machine were undertaken by A.G. Spalding and Brothers in 1901. Another noteworthy piece of exercise equipment was Narragansett Machine Company's hydraulic rowing machine, which was produced around 1910. Together, these three rowing machines played a significant role in the equipment offering of many athletic clubs and gyms.

The Schmidt Machine, developed by Adrian Schmidt

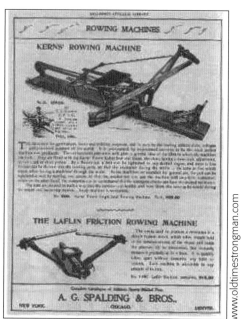

The Kern's & Laflin Rowing Machine, distributed by A.G. Spaulding and Brothers

One of the more unique and progressive pieces of fitness equipment to be developed during the first 30 years of the 20th century was the Exercycle, which was invented by Gordon Berg in 1932. Looking for a piece of equipment to use in combating a neuromuscular disorder that his wife inherited, Berg invented the Exercycle, which combined lower- and upper-body movements that simulated rowing, swimming, cycling, and chin-ups. The bike was powered by a small motor that allowed the user to go through a range of motion with varying levels of resistance. After developing the machine, he established the Exercycle Corporation, which manufactured and distributed his invention. The Exercycle subsequently became a prominent piece of equipment in many facilities during the 30s—achieving a level of popularity that lasted until the 70s. In some ways, Berg's Exercycle was a precursor of the Nu-Step and related semi-recumbent total-body exercisers of the late 20th century.

The early 20th century also brought about the advent of the mass production of fitness equipment and the establishment of industry-leading equipment brands. In 1902, Alan Calvert founded the Milo Barbell Company, the first company to mass produce barbells, dumbbells, kettlebells, and related strength training equipment. Subsequently, the Milo Barbell Company became the leading manufacturer of resistance equipment during the first three decades of the 20th century. What made this company unique was the variety of barbells and resistance equipment the entity produced, including barbells, such as globe bells, plate loaded bells, etc. Milo was the first company to introduce weight plates, rather than globes that had to be filled with shot, sand, or similar substance. The Milo Barbell Company not only produced barbells and dumbbells, it also manufactured pulley systems, medicine balls, etc. In 1935, the Milo Barbell Company's assets were sold to the York Barbell Company that was founded by Bob Hoffman.

The early 20th century also brought about the advent of the mass production of fitness equipment and the establishment of industry-leading equipment brands.

Another leading manufacturer of exercise-training equipment during the early 1900s was the Narragansett Machine Company of Rhode Island. First founded as a machine company in 1882, the Narragansett Machine Company entered the "fitness-equipment arena" in the early 20th century. By 1910, it was producing a comprehensive array of physical culture equipment, including barbells, dumbbells, Indian clubs, wall pulleys, climbing ladders, etc. In 1910, the company introduced the Narragansett Triplex, a three-way pulley system that allowed users to perform movements in multiple planes and from numerous angles (similar to today's functional pulley systems). Most of the equipment produced by Narragansett Machine Company was made of iron, brass, and oak.

In the 1930s, two new companies entered the arena of fitness equipment manufacturing--the Good Barbell Company and the York Barbell Company, both located in Pennsylvania. The Good Barbell Company, which opened in the late 1930s and operated till the 1970s, was founded by the Good Brothers, three successful strength athletes of the era. The York Barbell Company, founded in 1932 by Bob Hoffman, eventually became the leading manufacturer of weight equipment, especially after it purchased the assets of the Milo Barbell Company.

Clubs and Facilities of Distinction

The clubs that prospered during the period from 1900 to 1945 could generally be categorized into three distinct types. One distinct kind was the private member-owned athletic clubs that had opened in the late 1800s. Facilities in this group included such organizations as the Olympic Club of San Francisco, New York Athletic Club, Detroit Athletic Club, Los Angeles Athletic Club, Milwaukee Athletic Club, Chicago Athletic Association, and Downtown Athletic Club of New York (the former home of the Heisman). These clubs provided a blend of social companionship for elite businessmen and athletes, as well as an athletic environment for physical training. From an athletic perspective, these facilities offered fully equipped gyms, with gymnastic equipment, dumbbells, barbells, medicine balls, sport courts, and, in most cases, pools. The individuals who exercised in these clubs were focused on training for sport, as well as general health.

The second club category to prosper during this time period was the YMCAs, which, like the private athletic clubs, provided for both a social environment and a workout environment. The YMCAs differed from the athletic clubs in that their social focus tended to emanate from a "Christian spirit," rather than from an atmosphere of elitism or athletic prowess. On the other hand, gyms and athletic areas of YMCAs provided a training environment that was similar to those of the member-owned and -operated athletic clubs.

The third club category of health/fitness clubs that had its beginnings during this era was gyms. In reality, this third category of clubs—gyms—changed the course of the fitness business for decades to come. The gyms of this era were opened and operated by some of the most renowned strongmen and strength athletes of the time. One of the most famous gyms was Sig Klein's

Sig Klein's New York Studio of Physical Culture (1920s)

Studio of Physical Culture, which opened in 1927 in New York City. Sig Klein was a famous strongman (one of the few men to ever perform a one-hand overhead press of the famous Rolandow Challenge Barbell (299 pounds when filled). Klein was also a well-recognized strength and physical culture coach, who had formerly worked with Professor Attila, who had opened his New York gym (e.g., Attila's Athletic Studio and School of Physical Culture) in mid-town Manhattan in 1894. Upon Professor Attila's passing, Klein assumed ownership and management of the facility, reopening Attila's gym in 1926 and, shortly thereafter, opening his own Studio of Physical Culture in 1927 .

Klein's studio became the most popular gym on the East Coast, as well as home to many of the period's great strength athletes, and aspiring strongmen, bodybuilders, physical culturists and celebrities. The studio, which was located in the heart of midtown Manhattan (48th street and 7th avenue), operated for 50 years. During that span of 50 years, it remained one of the legendary gyms in New York. When discussing Sig Klein's gym, it would be a blunder not to note a few of Klein's other contributions to the health and fitness industry, including the development of the "feet press machine" (a prototype of the leg press machine introduced by York Barbell nearly a decade later); the development of

Professor Louis Attila's Athletic Studio and School of Physical Culture

the "iron boot;" and the development of the "in-Klein board." Klein published his own newsletter, the *Klein Bell* in the early 1930s, a publication that was extremely popular among strength enthusiasts.

In the late 20s and early 30s, two famous Philadelphia, Pennsylvania gyms opened their doors—Hermann's Gym and John Fritshe's Gym. These two Philadelphia facilities, along with Sig Klein's in New York, became the hotbeds of the early gym business, and "homes" to some of the most successful bodybuilders and strength athletes of the time. In the 1920s, about the same time Sig Klein's studio became popular, another well-known strongman, Harry Shafran, opened his first gym in New York. Shafran later developed a second gym in New York, operating both successfully for many years.

Another famous gym of the early 30s was the York Barbell Club Gym (Broad Street Gym) on Broad Street in York, Pennsylvania. As a facility to work out, this club was the home of some of America's greatest weightlifters and bodybuilders, including Tommy Kono, two-time Olympic Gold Medalist, and John Grimek, Mr. America and Mr. Universe). Over a period of 40 years, beginning in the early 1930s, the York Gym produced a significant number of accomplished weightlifters and some of the leading bodybuilders of the 40s, 50s, and 60s. Any mention of the York Barbell Club must include special homage to Bob Hoffman, the "Father of American Weightlifting." Hoffman founded York Barbell in 1932, concurrently with the publication of his renowned periodical, *Strength and Health Magazine*. Over the next 40 years, York Barbell became the mecca of weightlifting and bodybuilding in the United States, and possibly in the world.

In 1936, another legendary strongman, Jack LaLanne, opened his first club in Oakland, California. It was during the early years of his club that LaLanne created the modern versions of what is known today as the leg extension machine and Smith machine. LaLanne can also be given credit for beginning the migration of great gyms from the East Coast to the West Coast. LaLanne's impact on the industry, and fitness in general, did not really take hold for another 15 years, when he began hosting his nationally syndicated and highly popular television show, *The Jack LaLanne Show*.

Three years later in 1939, another well-known legend of the industry, Vic Tanny, along with his brother, Armand (a top bodybuilder of the time period), opened his first gym in Santa Monica, California. One year later, they opened a second gym in Long Beach, California. Unfortunately, World War II ultimately resulted in both clubs closing. Vic Tanny's contributions to the industry, similar to those of Jack LaLanne, did not really take hold till after the end of World War II.

One of the more unique clubs that opened during the 1930s was the Town Club in Chicago. The Town Club, located on North Michigan Avenue in Chicago, was initially owned by Robert Kendler, a legendary handball player, and one of the founding fathers of racquetball. During the 30s and 40s, the club was considered one of the meccas of handball. In 1944, this facility installed the first glass walls in its handball courts (courts that were subsequently converted to racquetball courts).

© Globe Photos/ZUMA Press

Jack LaLanne

An Outsider Whose Influence Would Not Be Felt for Decades

In the early part of the 20th century, a young man born in Germany of Greek descent, Joseph Pilates, pursued what might be considered the first form of cross training. Pilates blended the study of bodybuilding, boxing, martial arts, gymnastics, and yoga into an exercise routine that enabled him to develop a body that, by age 14, allowed him to serve as a model for anatomical charts. After achieving notoriety as an anatomical model in Germany, Pilates moved to England where he boxed, worked as a circus performer, and later was employed as a self defense instructor for the British military. During World War I, he was detained by the British as an "enemy alien." During his time in detention, he lead other detainees in organized exercise, using a system he referred to as "contrology," which, 30 years after his passing, would become one of the hottest fitness trends of the late 20th and early 21st centuries. While in detention, he worked in a hospital unit, where he helped rehabilitate injured soldiers. In the course of rehabilitating these soldiers, Pilates created special equipment that would allow them to exercise, while they were still hospitalized in a bed. It was this experience that led him to the development of today's modern-day Cadillac table.

Joseph Pilates in action

thepilatesflow.com

By the early 1920s, Pilates immigrated to New York, where he met his future wife, a nurse, during the course of his journey. Upon arriving in New York, the two were married and established a fitness studio, based on his program of "contrology." The studio opened in 1926 in the vicinity of the New York City Ballet. Initially, his studio attracted the most accomplished dancers of the period. Later, many of the nation's most well-known actors, circus performers, and boxers also sought out his expertise. The studio, operated for 50 years, closing only after his death in 1967. The studio was the training ground for a small, but passionate, group of devotees, including Ron Fletcher, Carola Trier, Kathy Grant, and Lolita San Miquel. It was not Pilates' intention to create a large network of "contrology" studios. As a result, his program lived on only as a result of the many students who developed their own studios—one of the most popular in this regard was Ron Fletcher's Studio that opened in Los Angeles in 1970. In 1967, Kathy Grant and Lolita San Miquel received degrees from the State University of New York to instruct "Pilates," representing the only two instructors believed to have been certified by Joseph Pilates. From these beginnings, Pilates would subsequently become one of the top forms of training in the world.

The Post-War Baby Boom
(1945 to 1970)

Chapter 4

"First we inspire, then we perspire.
Your waistline is your lifeline."

— Jack LaLanne

The Post-War Baby Boom, Suburbia, and Fitness for the Masses

At the end of World War II, life in the United States experienced a series of dramatic changes. First, the largest demographic generation of mankind (i.e., the baby boomers) would come into being as the result of a nation's desire to heal the wounds and loneliness created by the Great War. Second, the government of the U.S. poured large amounts of money into the creation of a national infrastructure, and with it, the creation of "suburbanization" and small town America. Third, a new "middle class" was created—a segment of the population where everyone had a home, a car, and a family, leading to the germination of what is now often termed "karaoke capitalism." Finally, a rapid development of technology occurred, which in a few short years, seemingly led to a television in every household and a car in every garage. As the nation changed, so did the world of fitness, transitioning out of private men's clubs and sweaty gyms into more mass market facilities and programs.

Artisans and Influencers of the Fitness Industry

As with every period in the history of fitness, certain innovators and individuals stand out as having had a significant influence on the development of the industry during this period. From 1945 to 1970, it was no different, as a handful of industry professionals set forth forces that would change the industry.

One person who exerted considerable influence in the 1930s was Bob Hoffman, who founded York Barbell Company. Known as the "father of American weightlifting," Hoffman, created a dynasty, over a period of 40 years, that had significant impact on fitness and the gym culture in America. In addition to founding one of America's most renowned weightlifting companies, he also published two of the most well-received publications of the period, *Strength and Health Magazine* and *Muscular Development*. Anyone who lived during this time period and pursued a regime of weightlifting or bodybuilding was significantly impacted by Bob Hoffman and the York Barbell Company.

Another legendary figure of the post-war baby boom years, and quite possibly the most influential fitness pioneer of this or any time period, was Jack LaLanne. In 1951, Jack LaLanne became the host of a nationally syndicated TV show called the *Jack LaLanne Show*, America's first telecast dedicated to the pursuit of fitness. LaLanne was a natural fit in this new medium, promoting the benefits of fitness. His combination of charisma, sense of humor, enthusiasm, knowledge, and, of course, physical appearance, made him a star. More significantly, LaLanne's show brought fitness into the homes of millions of Americans. Every morning across America, countless housewives, and even men, were "mesmerized" by the wholesome form of exercise that LaLanne preached. As a result, the gospel of living a fit lifestyle spread rapidly across America. Over the next 34 years, concluding in 1985, Jack LaLanne become the face of fitness. In addition to his fame as a TV personality, LaLanne's

> Anyone who lived during this time period and pursued a regime of weightlifting or bodybuilding was significantly impacted by Bob Hoffman and the York Barbell Company.

*The Jack LaLanne Show was America's
first nationally syndicated television
show dedicated to the pursuit of fitness.*

influences went much further. LaLanne is credited with having invented the "Smith machine" (named after Rudy Smith, a club pioneer who brought the piece to market) and the leg extension machine, both staples of the modern fitness center. LaLanne also had the most recognized name in the health spa and gym business. At one time, his name was associated with over 200 clubs, an effort that was initiated when he lent his name to Ray Wilson's European Health Spas, which then became Jack LaLanne European Health Spas. Years later, he licensed his name to Bally.

In 1957, Harold Zinkin, a former Mr. California, created and patented the Universal multi-station resistance machine. While not highly regarded at their inception, Universal machines subsequently went on to become one of the most popular pieces of exercise equipment in the world. Subsequently, Universal became the leading manufacturer of multi-station and related resistance equipment, appearing in gyms, schools, and military facilities around the world.

Harold Zinkin, on the cover of Bob Hoffman's
Strength and Health *magazine.*

Not until the late 1960s was the industry again rocked and changed forever by four individuals whose passion, creativity, and self-promotional acumen, touched the minds, bodies, and souls of health/fitness enthusiasts everywhere. The first of these individuals during this period, and possibly the most well-known or promoted of the four, was Kenneth Cooper, MD. Dr. Cooper is credited with coining the word "aerobics." His first book, *Aerobics*, published in 1968 was a worldwide bestseller. Dr. Cooper initially began his lifelong involvement in fitness as a member of the military as a flight surgeon and director of the Aerospace Medical Laboratory. During his tenure in these roles, he developed the 12-minute fitness test and 1.5-mile fitness test for cardiovascular capacity, both of which are still in use in the 21st century. Dr. Cooper is also renowned for creating "aerobic points," a systematic easy-to-use method of determining the relative amount of "work" performed, based on the mode, intensity, and duration of a specific bout of cardiovascular activity. In essence, Cooper established an entire genre of exercise and exercise equipment that is now referred to as aerobic activity.

Another particularly noteworthy individual during this period was Clark Hatch, who is known as the "Fitness Ambassador to Asia." Hatch opened his first fitness center in Tokyo, Japan in 1965. Over the next 45 years, Hatch opened, operated, managed, and licensed over 120 fitness centers in 14 different nations, most of them located in the Asia and Pacific regions. The first person to introduce a modern fitness center to Asia, Clark is considered by many individuals in the fitness industry to be the Jack LaLanne of Asia.

www.cooperaerobics.com

Kenneth Cooper

www.clarkhatch.com

Clark Hatch

Another ground-breaking entrepreneur and innovator of this period was Jackie Sorenson, who in 1969 developed what is today called "aerobic dancing." In the late 1960s, Sorenson was retained by the Air Force to create a fitness program for the wives of Air Force personnel. As an experienced dancer and a former Dallas Cowboy cheerleader, Sorenson took various dance-oriented movements and choreographed a complete exercise routine that was designed to enhance an individual's level of fitness, as well as be enjoyable to perform. Soon after, she also introduced her new program to the YMCA. The rest is history, as Jackie Sorenson became renowned as the creator of modern-day aerobic dancing.

Jackie Sorenson

www.jackis.com

© Joanna Jhanda/Contra Costa Times/ZUMA Press

Physical activity that incorporates music has become one of the most popular forms of exercising in the world (e.g., Jazzercise, ZUMBA, etc.)

In 1969, another pioneer and legendary figure in group exercise, Judi Sheppard Missett, burst onto the fitness scene, when she created Jazzercise. Missett developed her new form of exercising by blending movements from various activities, including dance, Pilates, yoga, and resistance training, and combining them to music. Over the next 40 years, Jazzercise evolved into the largest fitness franchise operation in the world, with over 32,000 classes annually in almost three dozen countries.

Outsiders Who Had an Immense Impact on the Industry

The first outsider from this era whose innovative thinking and efforts had a significant impact on the fitness industry was Joseph Sobek. Sobek helped pioneer American paddle tennis, or what he called "paddle racquets," which was played on a handball court. In 1957, Sobek established the National Paddle Racquets Association to serve the emerging sport. This unique sport, with some ongoing modifications initiated by Sobek, and later facilitated by the International Racquets Association (IRA), became the sport that is now called racquetball.

In 1968, Larry Lederman, director of the Milwaukee, Wisconsin Jewish Community Center, observed that his facility's handball courts were being used more for "paddle racquets" than for handball. Lederman, after reaching out to other facilities with handball courts, identified a growing national trend, which was the playing of paddle racquets on handball courts. Based on his observations, he organized the first "national paddle racquet championships" in November of 1968. Lederman, a board member of the U.S. Handball Association (USHA), sensing a rapidly changing tide in the use of handball courts, asked Robert Kendler, president of the USHA, and its executive secretary, Mort Leve, to visit his facility and observe this growing sport of paddle racquets. As a result of this visit, Kendler and Leve agreed to organize and promote the new sport. Kendler incorporated the International Racquets Association (IRA) in 1968, with Mort Leve serving as the association's first executive director. In 1969, the name paddle racquets was officially changed to racquetball. By 1970, Mort Leve, who was serving as the director of both the USHA and the fledgling IRA, retained his son, Chuck Leve, to be the new executive director of the IRA. Starting in 1970, the IRA, under the leadership of Chuck Leve, undertook the development and codification of rules and standards to govern the fledgling sport of racquetball. In 1974, the National Court Club Association (NCCA) was formed to represent the growing number of racquet clubs.

> By 1974, over three million people were participating in the sport. Racquetball would become the spark that was the genesis for an entire club industry segment in the 1970s.

By 1974, over three million people were participating in the sport. Racquetball would become the spark that was the genesis for an entire club industry segment in the 1970s. Subsequently, the NCCA, which represented racquetball clubs, became one of the two founding organizations that merged to create the International Racquet Sports Association (IRSA).

Another change-agent who appeared on the fitness landscape during this post-war period was Lotte Berk. Berk (born Liselotte Heymansohn in Cologne, Germany) was a professional ballet dancer in the 1920s and 1930s and later a professional dancer during the 40s and 50s in England. In the mid-50s, she collaborated with an osteopathic physician to create a series of exercises that were based on her experiences as a dancer. Her exercise techniques combined principles from Pilates and yoga, as well as her own dance background. Known as an eccentric and often caustic personality, Berk assigned her exercises names, such as "prostitute," "peeing dog," and "French lavatory." In 1959, Berk

www.telegraph.co.uk

Lotte Berk

opened an exercise studio in Manchester, England that she called Rehabilitative Exercise. The studio, with Berk leading the charge, taught her unique and intensive exercise program (focused on developing the "core"). Over the decades, numerous well-known individuals, especially women, flocked to her classes to learn her secrets for developing an incredible core and fantastic legs. In 1970, Lydia Bach, an avid fan of Lotte Berk's program, bought the worldwide rights to the Lotte Berk name and techniques. One year later, Bach opened a "Lotte Berk" studio in New York, New York. Some individuals refer to Lotte Berk as the "Queen of Fitness," though her influence as a fitness guru was somewhat limited, at least until the 21st century. On the other hand, it could reasonably be argued that the Lotte Berk method might be considered, along with Pilates, as the two modern founding exercise methods for developing the core.

Equipment Innovations and Equipment Manufacturers

During the 25-year time period, 1945 to 1970, fitness equipment experienced several important and enduring innovations.

❏   Cardiovascular Equipment

In 1952, Robert Bruce and Wayne Quinton developed the first commercial medical treadmill. Dr. Bruce, who was a faculty member at the University of Washington, and his colleague, Wayne Quinton, developed the treadmill for purposes of testing individuals for cardiovascular function. Their product, named the Quinton treadmill, was extremely well-constructed. In time, their treadmill became a staple of medical centers and universities that were involved in medical stress testing and human performance measurement. Nearly two decades later, in 1968, Bill Staub, a mechanical engineer, in cooperation with Kenneth Cooper, M.D., developed and sold the first commercial treadmills, which were called Pacemaster treadmills.

The 1950s and 60s witnessed the introduction of stationary indoor cycling as a means of pursuing personal fitness. In 1954, Monark, a Swedish company, introduced the first cycle ergometer. Developed by P.O. Astrand, Harry Hagelin, and Dr. William van Dobeln, the Monark cycle ergometer became one of the most widely used stationary cycles for conducting fitness-performance assessments, and later for providing basic stationary cycle workouts. In 1965, Schwinn Bicycle Company introduced its first in-home exercise bicycle to the public. In 1969, Tunturi, a Finnish company, introduced the W1 Exercise Bike. The W1 became the benchmark stationary cycle for home use, selling over one million bikes, which earned it the title of the world's best selling piece of home exercise equipment. The Tunturi W1 and later versions of the bike soon became a staple in many gyms and clubs around the world. In the process, it established a platform for other innovative indoor cycles that would be developed in the decades to come.

In 1968, Dr. Keene Dimmick created the Lifecycle exercise bike, the first computerized fitness bike of its kind. The Lifecycle had numerous unique features, particularly its use of technology and the 12-minute workout protocol it incorporated. Subsequently, the Lifecycle, which revolutionized the fitness industry, became the best-selling computerized fitness bicycle of all time. The Lifecycle did not hit full stride until Ray Wilson and Augie Nieto (two legendary figures in the health/fitness industry) established the framework for promoting and selling the bike to clubs in the early 1970s.

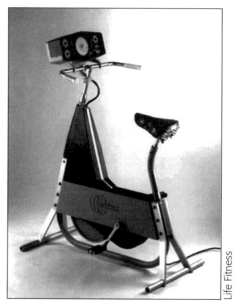

The first Lifecycle (1968)

Life Fitness

*The Universal Gym, a machine that had a revolutionary
impact on the fitness equipment industry.*

❏   Resistance Equipment

In 1957, Harold Zinkin, a former Mr. California, invented the Universal multi-station machine. The Universal machine was the first multi-station, selectorized piece of resistance equipment manufactured and sold in the world. Zinkin patented his equipment, and, shortly thereafter, introduced the first circuit weight training programs, performed on his machines. In 1960, he introduced the Mack series of multi-station machines, selling approximately one unit per month. By 1964, Universal was selling one unit per week. Zinkin sold his company in 1968. The new owners, however, continued to expand upon the Universal brand, introducing several exercise machine series over the decades to come. The term "dynamic variable resistance," representing the mode of resistance provided by their machines, was patented by Universal in 1974. Universal later evolved into a company that manufactured a full array of exercise equipment, including free-weight benches, single-station selectorized equipment, and cardiovascular machines (e.g., bikes, rowers, treadmills). During its heyday, universal was the leading seller of selectorized resistance equipment to schools, gyms, clubs, and YMCAs in the world.

    In the 1950s, Jack LaLanne created a piece of equipment that enabled the users to safely lift heavy weights. Industry pioneer Rudy Smith, an employee of Vic Tanny's, observed the machine and realized its potential. Subsequently, he developed it further, later introducing it to gyms and clubs across the country. The machine eventually was called the Smith machine in honor of Rudy's insight and efforts.

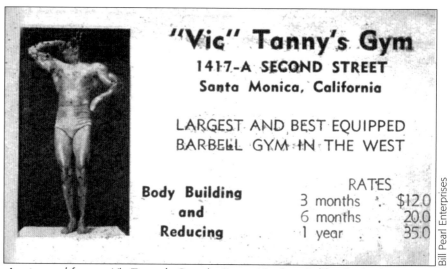

A rate card from a Vic Tanny's Gym in Santa Monica, California, in the 1940s

❑   A Unique Fitness Accessory

In 1963, an Italian plastic manufacturer, Aquilino Cosani, perfected the process of molding large puncture-resistant plastic balls. These balls, called "Pezzi balls," were adopted by a British physiotherapist, Mary Quinton, to use in treatment protocols for newborns and infants. Later, Dr. Susanne Klein-Vogelbach, the director at the Physical Therapy School in Basel, Switzerland, integrated the use of ball exercises into her physical therapy protocols for neuro-developmental treatment. This form of treatment was described by her as "functional kinetics," and was used to treat adults with orthopedic or similar kinetic challenges. The term "Swiss ball" was coined by American physical therapists when they adopted the use of the ball in their practices. Nearly 35 years later with the advent of functional training, the Swiss ball has become a staple in the toolkit of most personal trainers.

❑   Leading Manufacturers of the Era

The fitness equipment manufacturing industry of the 50s and 60s was still in its infancy. York Barbell was the most well-known and most successful manufacturer of weight training equipment, both for the home market and the commercial market. In the mid-50s, Paramount Fitness originated and began manufacturing free weight equipment and later resistance exercise machines that were sold to gyms, health spas, and athletic clubs. By the end of the 1960s, Universal Gym Equipment, which was founded in 1957, subsequently became the foremost equipment manufacturer in the industry.

U.S. Clubs and Facilities of Distinction (1945 to 1970)

After 1945, the private athletic clubs (primarily serving men) that were founded in the previous century continued to prosper, as did the numerous gyms established in the early 1900s to serve avid physical culture fans, such as bodybuilders and weightlifters. A number of clubs, such as the New York Athletic Club and the Olympic Club of San Francisco continued to have a loyal following, as did many small facilities, such as Sig Klein's in New York and the Broad Street Gym in York Pennsylvania.

A particularly noteworthy change in the health/fitness club industry involved Vic Tanny, who opened his first bodybuilding gym in Santa Monica, California in the early 1940s with $200 he borrowed from a friend. He opened a second club shortly thereafter, also in Southern California. These original clubs offered members 3-month, 6-month and annual memberships. At the outbreak of World War II, both clubs closed. As a consequence of his earlier experience and the conclusion of the Great War, Tanny saw a unique opportunity to open a new-style gym, based on the needs of a relatively "fresh" generation of consumers from the middle class. In 1947, Tanny opened his new type of gym in Los Angeles, a facility dedicated to serving the middle-class suburban market. His new clubs, aptly named Vic Tanny's, welcomed both men and women. This new type of club featured mirrors, carpet, chrome, saunas, pools, and gym areas. With these efforts, Tanny had created the first "modern health club." These new clubs sold memberships on contract, offering consumers the opportunity to purchase a six-month contract, or if they prefferred, a permanent seven-year contract. By 1960, Vic Tanny's had evolved from a single club to 84 clubs that collectively had approximately one million members and $24 million in annual sales ($176 million in 2011 dollars). In the process, Tanny's became the largest club operator in the U.S. and the first large-scale chain of clubs in America. Vic Tanny's also was the first U.S. club company to enter Europe, when in 1964, he opened a facility in Germany.

Vic Tanny's holds claim to being more than just the first modern health club or the first major chain of health clubs. Tanny's is also the father of the hard-sell, price-discounting, high-volume, do-anything-to-get-the-customer-to-join approach to membership sales. In an article that appeared in *Time* Magazine in 1961, Tanny is quoted as saying, "volume is what counts." In the same article, the author also quotes a phrase from one of the company's many memos that went to sales staff on a daily basis. In this particular notice, Tanny's leadership said, "If you fail to get an appointment, then take a gun out of the desk and shoot yourself." It was well understood among the sales staff and sales managers at Vic Tanny's that your job was to sell at all costs, to pressure prospects, to intimidate them, and no matter what, to make the sale. If someone sold more than you on a particular day, that person became the sales manager the next day.

In 1960, as a result of the numerous complaints received from Vic Tanny's members and customers, the New York State Attorney General persuaded all

Tanny's is also the father of the hard-sell, price-discounting, high-volume, do-anything-to-get-the-customer-to-join approach to membership sales.

gyms to sign a fair practices code that prohibited methods of selling that are deceitful, misleading, or fraudulent. This legacy of deceitful selling by Vic Tanny's, unfortunately, seems to have survived far longer than the other innovations that Tanny, himself, brought to the industry. In 1963, after reaching its pinnacle of 84 clubs and over $24 million in sales (over $176 million in current dollars), Vic Tanny's closed its doors, closing some clubs, and selling the balance to Health and Tennis Corporation, which was established one year earlier by Don Wildman, a former employee of Vic Tanny's (the company later became Bally Health and Tennis and finally Bally Total Fitness).

Only five short years after the creation of the Vic Tanny's chain, another pioneer and legend of the fitness club industry, Ray Wilson, developed what would become a successful series of health club chains. Starting in 1952 and continuing as late as 2005, Wilson created several distinct chains of clubs, some of which their legacy continues up until today (eventually operating over 270 clubs). During the 1950s, Wilson founded four club chains, and during the early 60s, another four chains. Among the club groups he founded and managed during the 50s and 60s were:

- American Health Studios, based in the U.S. and Canada, which operated from 1952 to 1958 and totaled 62 clubs at one point
- Silhouette Figure Salons, based in the U.S. and Canada, which operated from 1954 to 1958 and totaled 40 clubs at one point
- Silhouette International, based in Mexico, which eventually operated 15 clubs between 1958 and 1960
- Club International, located in Mexico, which eventually operated a dozen clubs, opened in 1958, and was operated by Wilson till 1960
- Trim and Swim Health Spas in Texas, which eventually operated a total of 14 clubs between 1960 and 1965
- President's Health Clubs in Texas from 1960 to 1965, which, at one point, operated 14 clubs
- European Health Spas, based in the United States, which opened in 1960 and by 1975 operated 46 clubs. It should be noted that Wilson later licensed the use of Jack LaLanne's name, a transaction that resulted in the clubs being marketed as Jack the LaLanne European Health Spas.
- European Health Spas, Canada, which opened in 1962, and by 1970 had 21 clubs

Wilson's facilities were patterned on the club concept that was originated by Vic Tanny when he established his health clubs in the late 1940s. Wilson's early clubs, which had small footprints and only one locker room, introduced the alternate-day concept for health clubs, wherein men used the clubs three days a week (usually Tuesday, Thursday, and Saturday), women used the club three days a week (typically Monday, Wednesday, and Friday), and on Sundays, the day was split between male and female members. Wilson also expanded on Tanny's club concept by incorporating saunas, steam rooms, spa pools (i.e., whirlpools, for which he takes credit for introducing), and recreational

> Only five short years after the creation of the Vic Tanny's chain, another pioneer and legend of the fitness club industry, Ray Wilson, developed what would become a successful series of health club chains.

pools. Like Vic Tanny, Wilson, capitalizing on the changing demographics and psychographics of America, was able to move clubs from a male-dominated bodybuilding and lifting culture to facilities that featured physical training, fitness, and a degree of pampering for both men and women. It should be noted that the clubs operated by Wilson also built on another aspect of the playbook created by Vic Tanny, which was to foster a "high-pressure" sales environment that encouraged, and even required, sales staff to use less-than-transparent approaches to selling memberships. Wilson's facilities also introduced the fitness facility industry to two new membership offerings. The first was the"lifetime membership," which allowed him to oversell his clubs (e.g., sell more memberships than the facility could realistically handle), and the second was a month-by-month membership offering.

Building on the legacy established initially by Vic Tanny and then by Ray Wilson, Don Wildman, a former Vic Tanny's employee, founded Health and Tennis Corporation in 1962. By 1963, he had acquired approximately one dozen Vic Tanny's clubs, thereby growing his company into one of the largest club-operating groups in the United States. Over the course of the 1960s and 1970s, Health and Tennis Corporation subsequently purchased other regional club operations, including the President's Health Clubs in Texas (formerly owned and operated by Ray Wilson and his associates). By the time the 1970s ended, Health and Tennis Corporation had acquired a number of regional club chains, including Jack LaLanne European Health Spas, Scandinavian Health Spas, and Holiday Universal. Health and Tennis Corporation's greatest impact on the industry would come in the late 1970s and 1980s. Wildman's organization reached its pinnacle of recognition when it was purchased in 1983 by Bally Manufacturing and became Bally Health and Tennis.

Two other club companies, both of which remain prominent in the 21st century, also laid their foundation for future success during the period of the 1960s. The first was Gold's Gym, founded by Joe Gold in 1965 in Venice, California. It was not until after Gold sold the club in 1970 (actually not until the 1980s), when its two new owners, Pete Grymkowski and Tim Kimber, began franchising the brand, that Gold's really took off as a global brand. Gold's opened its first franchise in 1980, and by 1988 had over 200 franchises. Currently, Gold's Gym has over 600 owned and franchised clubs throughout the world.

The second company to establish its foundation for future success during the 1960s was the Mid-Town Tennis Club of Chicago, opened by Alan Schwartz and his father, Kevie, in 1969. Mid-Town Tennis Club (the largest indoor tennis club in the world) became the flagship club for what would later become Tennis Corporation of America (sebsequently rebranded as Mid-Town Athletic Clubs). At first, Tennis Corporation of America established a specific niche that served the affluent tennis market. Initially, the company focused on its trademarked and patented program, "Tennis in No Time." Over the past couple of decades, however, the company has established a reputation for operating some of the best high-end, multipurpose clubs in the United States.

Over the past couple of decades, Tennis Corporation of America has established a reputation for operating some of the best high-end, multipurpose clubs in the United States.

International Fitness Centers of Distinction

The most distinguished and recognized international club company that established its roots in the 1960s (a company that remains prominent today) is Clark Hatch Fitness Centers. Clark Hatch, a former army veteran who had been

Clark Hatch Fitness Centers brought American-style fitness to Asia.

based in Korea, opened his first international club in 1965 in Tokyo, Japan. Seven years later, he established a second club in Seoul, South Korea. Over the next 45 years, he developed, operated, managed, and licensed over 120 centers in 14 countries. Clark Hatch Fitness Centers were the first "modern gyms" to enter the Asian market. Hatch's organization established a unique niche by developing relationships with the leading hotel groups that served the growing Asian market, including companies such as Hilton, Sheraton, and Sofitel. By locating his clubs primarily in upscale hotel complexes, Clark Hatch Fitness Centers were able to reach out to the first "wave" of U.S. expatriates to establish roots in Asia, and undertaking which, in the process, brought American-style fitness to Asia. Hatch is often referred to as the "Fitness Ambassador to Asia," and expatriates and Asian nationals know his centers for their "pleasingly professional" approach to treating the customer (a tagline that is a prominent part of the Clark Hatch mission statement).

Four years after Hatch opened his first fitness center in Tokyo, Japan, a company known as Central Sports opened its first club in the same market. Central Sports was the first company to introduce a western-styled fitness center with a uniquely "Japanese" feel (strong emphasis on an aquatic environment) to the Japanese market. Currently, 41 years after its inception, Central Sports owns and operates over 150 clubs that collectively have annual revenues of approximately $500 million, making it one of the 10 largest fitness companies globally by revenues.

About the same time period as Clark Hatch and Central Sports emerged in Japan, an innovative pioneer in Germany, Werner Keiser, founded his unique brand of niche clubs, Keiser Training, AG. Founded in 1967, Keiser's company took a unique approach to the club market by introducing a brand of clubs that emphasized the use of resistance-training circuit equipment to strengthen the core. These clubs had a small footprint, offered only one form of training protocol, and sold memberships for a very affordable price. Keiser Training currently operates well over 100 clubs throughout Germany, and is one of the most recognized club brands in Germany.

Baby Boomers Emerge—
The Evolution of ME
(1970 to 1990)

Chapter 5

*"The race to make one's physical
appearance stunning in order to be admired
is on in full force in America."*
— Louis Harris, Pollster

*"Health clubs have replaced the singles bar as the
most popular meet-market."*
— *Newsweek*, 1977

Baby Boomers Give Birth to the Modern Health/Fitness Club Industry

By 1970, members of the baby boomer generation were entering adolescence and young adulthood. As this massive generation of semi-entitled, rebellious, and anti-establishment young people embarked on a new stage in their lives, they often took the rest of America and the world with them. Over the next 20 years, this large "bubble" of baby boomers became the most influential generation in modern history, changing the beliefs and practices of an entire globe. As the baby boomers matured, so did the fitness industry, patterning its evolution after that of the growing baby boomer demographic.

The 1970s

"A new class has come among us that defines elitism in an entirely different manner. For this is the time of the physical elite, a class of American men, women, and children who are…exercising a little, moderate amount, or in staggering gulps."
— John Van Door, from
"An Intimidating New Class:
The Physical Elite,"
New York Magazine, 1978

> The 1970s mark what many historians of the fitness industry believe to be the inception of the modern era of the fitness industry.

The 1970s mark what many historians of the fitness industry believe to be the inception of the modern era of the fitness industry. During the next 20 years, the fitness industry underwent more changes than in any time in its history, often mimicking the rapid transformations that were occurring in society in general. As with any other generation that experienced change, the movement was led by numerous individuals who were able to bring their ideas to the marketplace in a manner that engaged the public. During the 1970s and 1980s, fitness took on a "public presence," effectively entering the American lexicon of popular culture. The fitness surge of the 1970s and 1980s was driven by a number of factors, including popular culture, celebrities, and a desire to be seen as "perfect"—a collective, pervasive attitude that was reinforced by leaders within the fitness facility and equipment industry.

Artisans and Influencers of the Decade

On the public side, one of the most influential fitness figures of the 70s was Jim Fixx. In the early 1970s, Fixx authored, *The Complete Book of Running*, which became a best-seller and fixated the country on jogging and running. While America's preoccupation with "aerobics" could be credited to Kenneth Cooper, MD, it was Fixx and his book that helped make jogging and running a household phenomenon. Over the next decade, running would become the "aerobic" activity of choice for many Americans. Not surprisingly, a number of individuals consider Fixx to be the "godfather" of running in America.

During the 70s, diet programs and books also became extremely popular, especially with the advent of the low-fat and high-protein diet. Some of the more popular diet programs promoted during the decade included the *Scarsdale Diet*, written by Herman Tarnower, *The Pritikin Diet*, developed by Nathan Pritikin, Ph.D., and *The Diet Revolution* and the *New Diet Revolution*, both of which were penned by Robert C. Atkins, MD. These various diet programs and their celebrity authors established a framework that would later help fuel America's obsession with dieting.

In 1974, a highly unlikely cultural icon of fitness arose on the fitness scene—Richard Simmons. A formerly obese young man from New Orleans, Simmons moved to Beverly Hills, California, where he established his own unique approach to weight loss, one that featured a combination of exercise and diet. In 1974, he developed a center he called, "Slimmons," to spread his gospel of exercise and diet. To support his personal message of wellness, Simmons entered the infomercial arena, producing an extensive series of videos and books on fitness. His fitness videos went on to sell over 20 million copies. In the process, several of his videos, including "Sweatin to the Oldies," "Dance Your Pants Off," and "Disco Sweat," became best-sellers. Besides producing over 50 videos, Simmons authored nine books, including the best-seller, *Never Say Diet*. As a result of his dynamic message, unique persona, and ability to use television to promote his message in an entertaining and non-intimidating fashion, Simmons became the Jack LaLanne of the 70s and 80s for many individuals. With his groundswell message, Simmons established himself as a fitness guru for the masses.

For many individuals, Richard Simmons became
the Jack LaLanne of the 70s and 80s.

Arnold Schwarzenegger

Another influential cultural and fitness figure of the 1970s was Arnold Schwarzenegger. Through his movie, *Pumping Iron*, which was released in 1977, Schwarzenegger introduced people to bodybuilding and fitness. While some individuals might not consider a seven-time Mr. Olympia as a key figure in the growth of the fitness industry, it was Schwarzengger's public persona that helped to foster a positive image for fitness and exercise among a young adult baby boomer population. To a great degree, Schwarzenegger helped initiate a relative rush to health/fitness facilities across America.

One of the first industry faces of the 1970s to change the fitness industry landscape was Arthur Jones, the inventor of the Nautilus Variable Resistance Machine. While Jones had been involved in fitness previously (having created a Nautilus protoype as early as the late 1940s), it was his revolutionary development of the Nautilus CAM and variable resistance that changed how people exercised, and how clubs and gyms presented their product to the marketplace. His efforts helped foster the development of the modern fitness-equipment company. Subsequently, his Nautilus Sports/Medical Products Company became the largest manufacturer of fitness equipment in the world, achieving annual sales of close to $75 to $80 million (equivalent to $250 to $270 million in 2011) at its pinnacle in the late 1970s. Truth be known, Jones' most significant contribution to the world of fitness may not have been the Nautilus equipment that he introduced in 1970. Rather, Jones' most lasting influence may well be the core principles of training that he developed and advocated, including performing one set of exercises to exhaustion, undertaking super slow controlled concentric and eccentric training, and engaging in 20-minute workout circuits.

Arthur Jones

Another pioneer and legend of the fitness industry in the early 1970s, a figure, who similar to Arthur Jones, changed the face of the fitness facility industry, was Augie Nieto. Nieto was the founder of Life Fitness and an early proponent of the Lifecyle. While Nieto was not the inventor of the Lifecycle, he was the first employee of Lifecycle, which was founded by Ray Wilson, who had invested $1 million to acquire the rights to Lifecycle from its creator, Dr. Keene Dimmick. As the first salesperson for Lifecycle, Augie introduced the bike to club owners. In the process, the Lifecycle changed the way many people exercised in clubs. By the late 1970s, the Lifecycle was the top selling piece of cardiovascular equipment in the industry. Augie later purchased Lifecycle from Ray Wilson, and renamed it Life Fitness, a company that would subsequently become the world's largest manufacturer of fitness-related equipment.

In 1975, two events of historical significance occurred in the world of fitness that would decades later change the landscape for exercise prescription and fitness professional certification. The first transpired in 1975, when the American College of Sports Medicine (originally founded in 1954) published the first edition of its *Guidelines for Graded Exercise Testing and Exercise Prescription*. This manual was the first text in the modern era to set forth specific guidelines concerning how to conduct graded exercise tests and to prescribe exercise that is grounded on evidence-based research. Currently in its eighth edition, this book has gone on to become the benchmark for health/fitness professionals around the world who are involved in the development of exercise prescriptions for both healthy people and those individuals who are classified as at risk. Concurrent with the publishing of this book, the American College of Sports Medicine also developed the first two modern certifications for health/fitness professionals—*Program Director* certification, for those individuals who are involved in rehabilitative exercise prescription and administration, and *Exercise Leader* certification, for personnel who work with healthy adults. These two certifications not only established a framework for future certifications from ACSM, but also for a host of certifications from other professional associations and organizations in the decades to come.

Equipment Innovations and Equipment Manufacturers of the Decade

❑ Cardiovascular Equipment

By 1974, the Lifecycle, originally developed in 1968 by Keene Dimick, had gone on to change the course of the health/fitness club industry. Except for Nautilus, the Lifecycle would be the most influential piece of equipment to come to market in the 1970s. Along with Nautilus, it would be one of the most noteworthy types of exercise machines to originate in the last half of the 20th century. In the process, under the entrepreneurial spirit and insights of Ray Wilson and Augie Nieto, the Lifecycle became a symbol of the fitness industry.

The Lifecyle offered both the fitness consumer and the health/fitness club operator an innovative approach to aerobic training. The Lifecycle 2000 was the first piece of aerobic training equipment on the market to feature a standardized program for aerobic training, a component the company referred to as the "12-minute program." In addition to the standardized program, users could also select their level of resistance, thereby allowing exercisers to thus personalize the intensity of their training regime. The first Lifecycles offered a couple of different 12-minute protocols (e.g., hill, interval, etc.) that users could follow by simply pushing a button and then pedaling along to the changing level of intensity provided by the programs. The 12-minute program and the ability to adjust the intensity level revolutionized the approach that most manufacturers would subsequently follow when developing their company's cardiovascular equipment. One of the more unique aspects of the introduction of the Lifecycle to the market was the parent company's (Life Fitness) use of celebrities, including actors, such as Sylvester Stalone, to serve as spokespeople for the equipment. By the late 1970s, almost every health/fitness club in America had at least one Lifecycle and one Nautilus circuit.

> By the late 1970s, almost every health/ fitness club in America had at least one Lifecycle and one Nautilus circuit.

Approximately the time that the Lifecycle was introduced to the health/fitness club industry, another pioneering company, Trotter, entered the industry with a new club-friendly piece of aerobic training equipment. In 1973, Trotter introduced a revolutionary treadmill that was developed by the founder of the company, Edwin Trotter. Trotter was not the first company to enter the commercial market. In fact, Quinton had entered the medical market in 1952 and Pacer had gotten into the commercial treadmill market in 1968. Trotter's efforts were original, however, because the company developed a very easy and user-friendly treadmill that appealed to the average consumer and members of health/fitness clubs. During the 1970s and 1980s, Trotter would continue to expand its influence as a treadmill manufacturer. In the 1990s, it acquired the assets of another leading equipment company in the industry, when it purchased Cybex.

One year after Trotter entered the cardiovascular equipment business, another innovative company, Woodway, also introduced a treadmill to the market. In 1974, Willi Schoenberger developed a treadmill that had a unique running surface that he referred to as "Waldweg way of the Woods," producing a sensation that Schoenberger likened to running on pine needles. As such, the Woodway featured a revolutionary approach to treadmill design.

In 1975, Edward Pauls, a cross-country skiing enthusiast who was looking for a way to train year-round, founded PSI Nordic Track, Inc. In the process, Pauls created the Nordic Track Cross-Country Ski Machine, a relatively simple machine that closely simulated the movements of cross-country skiing outdoors. His innovation, which involved the use of wood skis mounted on a special track with a flywheel and a one-way clutch mechanism, introduced an entirely new means of indoor aerobic training to the health/fitness club industry. By the mid-1980s, Pauls' company achieved annual sales of over $15 million (equal to approximately $40 million in 2011 dollars), making his machines one of the most popular forms of aerobic training in clubs and homes.

In 1978, another noteworthy company entered the market for cardiovascular equipment in the health/fitness club industry—Trackmaster. Trackmaster was the fourth company to introduce a treadmill to the market during this particular period.

Another exceptional piece of cardio equipment that was introduced during the latter part of the 1970s was the Schwinn Airdyne. The Airdyne was a unique type of indoor bicycle that offered users two unique features. First, it provided friction-free air resistance, rather than the standard mechanical resistance offered by other bicycles. Second, it included both upper- and lower-body movement, thus affording a form of cross-training apparatus, rather than a mere bicycle. Relatively quickly, the Airdyne became extremely popular among older exercisers, as well as with some individuals with certain health conditions. Other than the Lifecycle, it may have been the most popular stationary bicycle of its generation.

Lifecycles

The Schwinn Airdyne

❑ Resistance Training Equipment

The most well-known and possibly most influential equipment innovation of the 1970s, and possibly of the last half of the 20th century, was the Nautilus machine. Arthur Jones, the founder of Nautilus, initially developed the concept for his machine nearly two decades earlier. Introduced to the world in 1970, Nautilus machines were significantly different than anything else on the market before them. One particular unique feature of these exercise machines was the Nautilus CAM, a specially designed pulley mechanism that was shaped like a nautilus shell (hence the name Nautilus). When a cable with weights was pulled over the CAM, the resistance experienced by the user varied, which, according to Jones, simulated the natural strength curve of a muscle group going through its normal range of motion. The term variable resistance was coined by Nautilus to explain the adjustment in resistance that was experienced by Nautilus users as they performed movements on the various machines.

In addition to the CAM, Nautilus' efforts to design and manufacture individual training machines for various body parts also had a significant impact on the industry. This series of machines enabled exercisers to train the body's muscle groups—one machine and one particular body area (circuit-style) at a time. The Nautilus machines offered an effective and efficient way for individuals to engage in resistance training. The combination of the CAM and the dedicated machines for each body part drove an entire segment of the health/fitness facility industry in the 1970s.

In a relatively short period of time, Nautilus machines became the generic symbol for resistance training machines (e.g, "Kleenex") for the fitness equipment industry. By the late 1970s, many consumers were walking into health/fitness clubs, asking if they had Nautilus equipment. Shortly thereafter, the industry experienced the rise of Nautilus Fitness Centers. Nautilus was also one of the first equipment manufacturers to take marketing to the next level by recruiting athletes and celebrities to promote its equipment. During the 1970s, many of the world's best known bodybuilding competitors endorsed and used Nautilus equipment. Nautilus was sold by Arthur Jones in 1986 to Travis Wood for an estimated $23 million, or approximately 33% of the annual revenues that the company had generated during its peak sales in the late 1970s.

Nautilus

The Nautilus "blue monster"

Nautilus

*An early version of the Nautilus
leg extension machine*

In 1978, the fitness industry experienced a second significant resistance equipment innovation, sparked by two brothers, Dennis and Randy Keiser, who had formed Keiser Corporation the previous year. Dennis, an engineer, who had worked previously on the development of weight-bearing resistance equipment for other manufacturers, developed and patented a compressed air pneumatic machine. In 1978, the brothers introduced the Keiser line of resistance equipment, the first line of resistance training equipment to offer athletes and average users alike a no-load form of resistance training. In reality, Keiser equipment featured several unique resistance-training innovations, including no-shock impact, weight increments as little as one pound, the ability to measure resistance, the capacity to train at variable speeds, the capability to instantly adjust the level of resistance (thereby allowing for different loads for concentric and eccentric training), and the opportunity to engage unilateral and bilateral training at different loads. When it was initially introduced, the Keiser equipment was quite popular among many athletes for its ability to train individuals with special developmental needs, such as strength, speed, and power. Subsequently, a number of segments of the health/fitness professional community, as well as the health/fitness club industry, also came to appreciate its value as a training tool for the elderly, women, and people with disabilities.

Keiser

The Keiser seated leg curl machine

Facilities of Distinction

❑   Health Spas

The 1970s was the beginning of what today is considered the modern era of the health/fitness club industry. The industry's most dominant player of the decade was Health and Tennis Corporation, founded in 1962 by John Wildman. During the 1970s, Health and Tennis Corporation acquired numerous other regional club chains, including Jack LaLanne European Health Spas, Scandinavian Health Spas, and Holiday Universal. During this decade, the various chains that were part of the Health and Tennis Corporation, each operating under its original brand (e.g., Presidents, Holiday Universal, Vic Tanny, Jack LaLanne European Health Spas, etc.), collectively grew into the largest club company in the industry. The company's clubs were particularly well-known for their "hard-sell" approach and their often unscrupulous approaches to selling memberships. Despite this set of circumstances, these facilities were considered the face of the club industry during the 1970s and 80s. In the early 1980s, after being purchased by Bally Entertainment, the company changed its name to Bally Health and Tennis.

> The 1970s was the beginning of what today is considered the modern era of the health/fitness club industry.

Another leading club company of the 1970s was Ray Wilson's Family Fitness Centers of California, founded in 1977. While the Family Fitness Centers were built along the lines of Wilson's early club groups, such as European Health Spas, they represented a different approach to market positioning. Whereas Wilson's previous club ventures featured both male and female access, the Family Fitness Centers targeted the entire family, without the inconvenience of alternate-day usage. By the time his clubs were sold in 1995 to 24-Hour Fitness, Wilson was operating approximately 72 Family Fitness Centers throughout California.

Along the lines of Health and Tennis and Family Fitness Centers, New York Health and Racquet Club was founded in the 1970s. These facilities, similar to the clubs operated earlier by Ray Wilson and Don Wildman, ushered in co-ed health/fitness facilities. New York Health and Racquet became one of the first multipurpose club chains to integrate pools, racquet courts, and gyms into one facility.

An interesting consequence resulting from the rapid growth of health club groups, such as Health and Tennis, European Health Spas, Scandinavian Health Spas and President's Health & Racquet, was the formation of the Association of Physical Fitness Centers (APFC). APFC was established in 1974 by Jimmy Johnson, an associate professor of business at the University of Maryland. This newly formed association served as a public advocacy group for the fledgling "health spa" segment of the fitness industry, which by the latter half of the 1970s, found itself facing potential industry regulation from the Federal Trade Commission, as well as by each state, as a result widespread problems within the industry (e.g., false and deceptive advertising practices, unfair cancellations and other deceptive business practices).

❏   Niche Health & Fitness Clubs

During the 1970s, the health/fitness club business began to look outside the standard club model that was pioneered and mastered by legends in the field, such as Vic Tanny, Ray Wilson, and Don Wildman, and the facilities of industry pioneers, such as Sig Klein and Jack LaLanne. While health spas, as they were often termed by the original industry pathfinders, prospered in the 1970s, other pioneering individuals sought out new niches.

One of the first entrepreneurs to identify a market niche and build on it was Lucille Roberts. In the early 1970s, Roberts, an emigrant from Russia, started the first chain of women's-only health clubs, with the founding of Lucille Roberts Health Clubs. Roberts' clubs set themselves apart by claiming to provide women with a club experience that focused on enriching their lives physically, emotionally, and financially. Her facilities offered a large variety of group classes, weight-loss programs, and children's sitting services. Roberts' health clubs are still in operation, 38 years after her first club opened.

In 1975, another enterprising individual, Michael O'Shea, Ph.D., founded the Sports Training Institute of New York. The Sports Training Institute represented a new business model that integrated physical therapy and personal training. The Sports Training Institute was the first facility to leverage personal training into a profitable business, while also incorporating a medical model into its business plan by having physical therapy as a core element of its client offering. The Sports Training Institute sold personal training and therapy, not memberships. As a result, it was one of the first modern clubs to focus on selling an outcome-driven product, instead of a membership. O'Shea's clubs were the first to require its trainers to have a college degree, a stipulation that even today would be somewhat unique to the industry. Furthermore, all clients of the Institute had to receive medical clearance before they could undergo a fitness evaluation and start their training. By the middle of the 80s, O'Shea had opened 10 facilities.

Mike O'Shea, whose Sports Training Institute was the first facility to leverage personal training into a profitable business

Cardio Fitness Centers were the first health/fitness facilities to focus on selling corporate memberships by working directly with large corporations and offering a custom membership package for executives.

In 1977, another unique brand of fitness club was brought to market in New York—Cardio Fitness Centers. Cardio Fitness Centers, pioneered by Dr. Jerry Zuckerman, introduced a new concept in fitness, one that targeted business executives. Zuckerman's fitness centers offered members a one-stop shop for pursuing cardiovascular conditioning and featured a number of desirable amenities, such as standard uniforms for all members (these uniforms were washed at the club and members selected a new uniform each day), permanent lockers for storing valuables and various workout items, fitness testing and stress testing for each member, and trained exercise physiologists as staff members (master's-degreed exercise physiologists to guide members through their workouts). Another unique feature of the Cardio Fitness Center experience involved scheduling members for two to three appointments each week (each appointment was 45 minutes in duration). Cardio Fitness Centers were the first health/fitness facilities to focus on selling corporate memberships by working directly with large corporations and offering a custom membership package for executives. Cardio Fitness was sold to H.J. Heinz in 1985 for approximately $50 million or $10 million per facility. In current dollars, this transaction would involve a price tag of over $100 million or over $20 million per site (undoubtedly one of the highest prices ever paid for a club chain on an individual-club basis).

Another pioneering firm that also got its start focusing on the corporate arena was Fitcorp, which opened its doors in 1979. Founded by Gary Klencheski, Fitcorp initially began as a firm that opened clubs in the Boston area that were specifically targeted to the corporate market (somewhat similar to the Cardio Fitness Centers of New York), and later expanded into managing on-site fitness centers for corporations that contracted its services.

Racquet Clubs Blossom

Two other niche club models that emerged in the 1970s were the indoor racquet-sport club and the indoor tennis club.

❑ Racquetball Clubs

The first club built specifically for the game of racquetball was King's Court in Minneapolis, Minnesota, which opened in 1970. Over the next few years, numerous indoor-sport clubs were developed across the country. Among the most reknown racquetball clubs to open during the 70s were Mel Gorham's Court Club in Pacific Beach, California, which opened in 1971; George Brown's racquetball club, San Diego, California, which opened in 1971, Gorham's Sports Center in Oceanside, California, which opened in 1973; Ken Rosland's club in Edina, Minnesota, which opened in 1973; John Wineman's and Bob Fitzgerald's Court House in Chicago, Illinois, which opened around 1974; Chuck Spalding's club in Saint Louis, Missouri; Pat McPharland's club (32 court club), Detroit, Michigan; The Racquet Clubs of Wisconsin, which opened in 1976 by Ted Torcevia; and the San Francisco Bay Club, San Francisco, California, which opened in 1977. A list of other pioneering racquet clubs includes The Racquetball and Handball Clubs of San Antonio, San Antonio, Texas; The Court Royal Clubs of Washington, DC; and the Racquetball and Sports Clubs of Atlanta, Georgia, which were developed by Norm Cates, Rich Boggs, and their partners.

The earliest racquet clubs typically included a central locker room area and eight racquet courts, four on each side of the locker room. Several of these new racquet clubs were actually renovations of existing handball clubs, while others were the result of new development efforts, based on the sport's growing popularity. As the industry evolved, larger court clubs were built, sometimes with as many as 22 to 32 courts. The financial model for the racquet club industry revolved around a "pay-for-play" model, which meant clients did not pay dues or annual fees (a model used by health spas of the period), but rather paid a set fee for a specified period of court time. The more a client played, the more that individual paid. Toward the turn of the decade, operators began to move to using Electronic Funds Transfer (e.g., EFT), a business model with monthly dues and lower court-fee costs.

Mort Leve, former executive director of the IRA and executive secretary of the USHA, saw the need to organize the fledgling racquet-court industry. In response, he established the National Court Club Association (NCCA) in 1974. By 1977, the NCCA was actively involved in promoting the interests of the racquet-court club industry. By 1978, after only five years, the racquetball craze began to fade, which caused club owners to begin converting courts into fitness zones, a practice that helped create the first multi-sport clubs. It was during this time period that Electronic Funds Transfer (EFT) evolved as a means of paying dues, and which, along with the growth in fitness, helped drive the establishment of multipurpose clubs (clubs with fitness and racquet sports). In 1981, the NCCA, under the leadership of executive director Chuck Leve, joined with the National Indoor Tennis Association (NITA), an organization that was lead by executive director Mary Johnson, which represented tennis clubs, to form IRSA, the International Racquet Sport Association.

By 1978, after only five years, the racquetball craze began to fade, which caused club owners to begin converting courts into fitness zones, a practice that helped create the first multi-sport clubs.

❑ Indoor Tennis Clubs

The second niche club market that grew rapidly during the 70s was the indoor tennis club. The Mid-Town Tennis club of Chicago, developed by Alan Schwartz in 1969 and opened to members in 1970, established a framework that was quickly adopted by others. Over the next two years, industry pioneers Curt Beusman, Dale Dibble and Todd Pulis opened their respective tennis clubs, Saw Mill Racquet Club in Mount Kisco, New York; Cedardale Athletic Club in Haverhill, Massachusetts, and the Thoreau Club in Concord, Massachusetts. These facilities which began as exceptional indoor tennis clubs, evolved over the following decades into industry-leading multipurpose clubs that delivered great tennis programming. Over the next decade, indoor tennis facilities, as well as indoor racquet clubs, which combined facilities for racquetball and

> The 1970s was a dynamic period of growth for the health/fitness club industry, with the emergence of numerous firms that continue to operate in the 21st century.

tennis, became an emerging and popular segment of the club industry. By the early 1980s, these clubs became pioneers of the multi-sport club industry that combined indoor racquet sports (e.g., racquetball and tennis) with fitness.

Other Pioneering Clubs and Club Firms of the 1970s

The 1970s was a dynamic period of growth for the health/fitness club industry, with the emergence of numerous firms that continue to operate in the 21st century. While many of these groups may not be known today as unique or pioneering, they deserve a footnote in the history of the industry as a result of their longevity and ability to evolve as they serve their respective markets. One example of these facilities was Powerhouse Gyms, which was founded in 1975 by the Dabish family of Detroit. Powerhouse Gyms developed a highly successful business model for gyms that focused on appealing to the serious weightlifter and bodybuilder. In the process, Powerhouse Gyms rivaled Gold's for supremacy in the licensing and franchising of gyms. By the 21st century, over 300 Powerhouse Gyms had been established.

Three other clubs and club companies of particular distinction that were founded during the 1970s were:

- Sport & Health, Washington, D.C. area, opened in 1973. Sport & Health was originally founded as a series of multipurpose clubs that included both racquetball and tennis.
- Town Sports International, New York, inaugurated in 1973. Originally, the company operated one racquet club in mid-town Manhattan. Subsequently, the organization became Town Sports International, operating New York Sports, Boston Sports, Washington Sports, and Philadelphia Sports.
- Houstonian, Houston, Texas, opened in 1978. This facility was initially developed to serve the emerging market of millionaires that was created by the oil boom of the 70s. Over the years, the club has been managed by several different owners, including Tom Fatjo, founder of Waste Management, Inc., who used the club as a model for his Living Well concept, a facility dedicated to the concept of Wellness. In the 1990s, the facility was purchased by the Redstone Group and developed into a premier luxury club in the United States (as of 2010, the joining fee for the club was over $30,000).

A Hybrid Sport Club Emerges

Another unique and inovative club concept that rose to prominence in the 1970s was the "City Athletic" Club developed by Club Corporation of America (CCA). CCA was originally founded by Robert Dedman in 1957 as a golf and country club company. By the early 1970s, with the emergence of indoor racquet sports and fitness, CCA ventured into a new arena, City Athletic Clubs. City Athletic Clubs were a hybrid form of a multi-sport club that combined indoor racquet sports (e.g., racquetball, squash, tennis), fitness, and fine dining (each facility had a formal dining area for business and social entertaining). Some of CCA's earliest City Athletic Clubs included the Universtiy Club, Jacksonville, Florida (1968); the University Club, Houston, Texas (1971); and the Metropolitan Racquet Club, Houston, Texas. By the 1990s, CCA had over thirty City Athletic Clubs in its portfolio.

A Unique Brand of Non-Commercial Fitness Center

The 1970s also brought about a unique type of fitness center, the corporate fitness center. In the early 1970s, companies, such as Kimberly Clark, Honeywell, Pepsico, and Johnson & Johnson, established fitness centers on their corporate campuses. By the late 1970's, at least 100 of these corporate fitness centers existed around the country, serving the needs of their company's employees. Subsequently, the demand for professional management of these corporate-owned facilities took off, resulting in the creation of the first company dedicated to managing corporate-owned fitness centers, Fitness Systems. Founded in 1975 by William Horton, Fitness Systems became the largest corporate fitness-center management firm in the world. Fitness Systems pioneered the way for other groups to enter this specific niche of the market over the next two decades, including firms, such as Health Fitness Corporation (founded in 1981 by Loren Brink), Medifit, and Plus One. About the same time that William Horton founded Fitness Systems, the Association of Fitness Directors in Business and Industry (AAFDBI) was formed to provide fitness professionals who were working in the corporate fitness field with professional networking and development opportunities.

The Global Fitness Club Market Evolves

The 1970s also experienced the rapid development of western-style fitness clubs in foreign markets. Among the most prominent, as well as the most respected, foreign players to evolve during this period, and coincidently, still operating as of 2011, include the following companies:

- Konami Sports & Life, Tokyo, Japan, founded in 1973. Originally, a part of the much larger People Company, Konami Sports & Life arose in the early 1970s and quickly expanded in Tokyo and across Japan.
- Goodlife Fitness Centers of Canada, founded in 1979 by David Patchell Evans. Evans' clubs have evolved into a large company, with over 200 clubs located in major urban areas, including smaller secondary markets.
- Renaissance, Inc. of Tokyo, Japan, opened in 1979. Subsequently, Renaissance became one of the "Big Three" in Japan, along with Central Sports and Konami Sports & Life.
- Organizacion Britania, Mexico opened in 1975. Subsequently, the company has become the largest club operator in Mexico with over 50 facilities.

> The 1970s also experienced the rapid development of western-style fitness clubs in foreign markets.

The 1980s

Artisans and Influencers of the Decade

By the time the 1980s arrived, baby boomers were in full bloom. The oldest generation of baby boomers where reaching their early thirties, while the youngest were in their mid-teens. In reality, much of what influenced this period of the fitness industry was directly related to the baby boomers and the "culture" of the times.

❏ People

One of the most prominent figures of popular culture to influence the fitness industry during the 80s was Jane Fonda. Fonda's most prominent effort in this regard was the release of her first video and book both entitled, *Jane Fonda's Workout*, in 1982. The Jane Fonda Workout became an instant hit, selling over 17 million copies and creating a craze in "high-impact" aerobics. In 1983, Fonda produced her second workout program, *Jane Fonda's Pregnancy, Birth, and Recovery Workout*. During the next decade, she would go on to release 23 videos and numerous books on fitness. In the process (appropriately or not), she became the symbol of "aerobic" classes during the 1980s.

© KEYSTONE Pictures USA/ZUMA Press

Jane Fonda, the symbol of "aerobic" classes during the 1980s

Jake Steinfeld

Another popular cultural icon of the 1980s who also had a significant influence on the growth of fitness was Jake Steinfeld. Founder of "Body by Jake," Steinfeld was a personal trainer, who in the late 70s and early 80s was training clients in Hollywood. At some point, his services were given to Stephen Spielberg as a birthday gift in the early 1980s. From that point on, Steinfeld's career blossomed, as he became a trainer of the stars and, shortly afterward, a celebrity himself. Steinfeld hosted his own television show, "Body by Jake," which became extremely popular. Steinfeld was also one of the first celebrities to license his name for use with various fitness products sold through infomercials. During the 80s, his celebrity grew through small parts in movies, such as the film *The Money Pit*, which was released in 1986, and *Coming to America*, which had its initial showing in 1988. Steinfeld's appearances in movies, as the host of his own TV show, and his involvement in numerous infomercials made him a "media star." His catch phrase, *"Don't quit,"* resonated with people who strived to change their lives through exercise. Possibly, his greatest achievement was creating Fit TV, which was eventually sold for $500 million.

Another dynamic personality of the 80's was Richard Simmons, who initially came to prominence in the 1970s and continued to exert enormous influence as a fitness celebrity In the ensuing decade. Simmons, like Jane Fonda capitalized on the use of infomercials to extend his reach to millions and thereby propagate the positive attributes of an active lifestyle.

While not an individual, another prominent cultural persona that influenced the fitness industry during the 1980s was the movie *Perfect*, starring Jamie Lee Curtis and John Travolta. Released in 1987, this film symbolized health/fitness clubs as the modern social environment for meeting individuals of the opposite gender (facilities sometimes referred to as the pick-up place of the 80s). One particular quote from the movie that stands out as an omen for what fitness would became in the 1980s, was uttered by John Travolta's character who proclaimed, "It was the physical great awakening."

John McCarthy, whose passion and insights helped establish the health/fitness club industry as an integral part of American culture

One of the most prominent industry faces of the 1980s was John McCarthy, the Executive Director of IRSA (International Racquet Sports Association). IRSA was founded in 1981 through a merger of sorts between the National Court Club Association and the National Indoor Tennis Association. Upon the creation of IRSA, the two founding organizations were discontinued. McCarthy served as the initial spokesperson for the fledgling industry association. Both his passion for the industry and his commitment to growing the industry helped to firmly establish the health/fitness club business as an integral part of American culture. McCarthy's legacy will be his passion for the business, his incredible gift at building relationships with everyone in the industry, and his commitment to pushing club owners and operators to expand their horizons, with regard to developing the future of the industry.

During McCarthy's tenure as the Executive Director of IRSA, a number of other club industry leaders, who were actively involved in founding IRSA in 1981, also helped to influence the course of the industry's history. A list of these luminary pioneers includes individuals, such as Curt Beusman, Rick Caro, Norm Cates (the first IHRSA president), Dale Dibble, Todd Pulis, Peter Donahue, and Jennifer Wayt-Saslaw.

Two additional individuals who had a significant impact on the industry during this period were Nickolas Orlando and Randy Peterson, founders of Randall Sports/Medical Products, Inc. These two forward-thinking entrepreneurs, while managing the distribution efforts in the Northeast region for Nautilus products, subsequently approached the inventor of the original StairMaster, and obtained exclusive rights to redesign and distribute his fledgling StairMaster product to the market. Upon the formation of the new company, Orlando and Peterson applied their knowledge of exercise and their marketing savvy to build StairMaster into the most popular piece of exercise equipment in health/fitness clubs in the world, and later into one of the leading equipment manufacturers in the entire fitness industry. A recent article that appeared in *USA Today* summed up the influence that StairMaster and its two innovative leaders, Orlando and Peterson, had on the industry in the 80s, when it started, "The invention was credited for being among the first machines to turn gyms into modern exercise arenas."

Another influential fitness figure of the late 1980s was Johnny Goldberg, an individual who is known to fitness professionals as Johnny G. Goldberg created one of the most viral group fitness programs in history when he developed Spinning in 1987. His enthusiasm, passion, and work ethic made Spinning a household name shortly after it was introduced. Over the course of the next decade, it became a staple in nearly every club that offered group exercise.

Johnny G, the developer of Spinning

❑ Associations

Up until the 1980s, talented, entrepreneurial individuals tended to exert the most influence on the fitness industry. Starting in the 1980s, however, professional associations of people and businesses started undertaking a more prominent role in shaping the course of the health/fitness club industry. Among the numerous organizations that were either founded or emerged in the 1980s, and had considerable impact on the industry's future, were the following six prominent professional groups:

- *Aerobics and Fitness Association of America (AFAA)*. Founded in 1983, this association started out as an educational provider, delivering workshops and educational materials for aerobic exercise professionals. Over the years, the association expanded its reach to serve both aerobic and fitness instructors. Currently, it develops educational workshops, educational literature, and certifications for fitness professionals. At one time, AFAA was the largest certifying body for group-exercise instructors in the world and remains one of the larger educational providers worldwide for fitness professionals.

- *American Council on Exercise (ACE)*. Founded in 1985 as a spinoff of the IDEA Foundation. ACE is an organization that is primarily dedicated to certifying and educating fitness professionals around the globe, as well as serving as an information resource on health and wellness to the American public. It is currently the largest certifying organization in the world, certifying personal trainers, group-exercise instructors, and other fitness professionals.

- *American College of Sports Medicine (ACSM)*. This organization was originally founded in 1954. In 1975, the college developed the first edition of its renowned publication, *ACSM's Guidelines for Exercise Testing and Prescription*, as well as its first two fitness certifications—program director and exercise leader. It was not until the 1980s when its certifications increased in demand and expanded, and fitness professionals began utilizing its *Guidelines for Exercise Testing and Prescription*, that the college's role in the industry took hold.

- *International Dance Exercise Association (IDEA)*. Co-founded in 1982 by Peter Davis and Kathie Davis as an association for group-exercise professionals. Over the years, IDEA expanded its audience to include personal trainers and other fitness professionals. Concurrently, they expanded their range of services to include an international convention and trade show, educational events, and the publication of a targeted magazine and other educational materials. IDEA originally created the IDEA Foundation for certifying fitness professionals, which was later spun off as the American Council on Exercise, an independent certifying organization. The association later changed its name to IDEA Health and Fitness Association.

- *International Racquet Sport Association (IRSA, later changed to IHRSA)*. Founded in 1981 using the elements of the preceedent organizations of the National Court Club Association and the National Indoor Tennis Association. Early in its history, the Association defined itself as the Association of Quality Clubs, which focused on serving the for-profit clubs

Starting in the 1980s, however, professional associations of people and businesses started undertaking a more prominent role in shaping the course of the health/fitness club industry.

*IHRSA is the face of the industry and the leading global
representative for the interests of the health/fitness club industry.*

whose values and business practices stood for quality and ethics. Over the years, the Association evolved, becoming an organization that promoted and protected the interests of the industry. By the mid-1990s, when it changed its name to IHRSA (International Health, Racquet and Sportclub Association), the Association had become the face of the industry and the leading global representative for the interests of the health/fitness club industry.

• *National Strength and Conditioning Association (formerly National Strength Coaches Association (NSCA).* Originally founded in 1978 to represent professional strength coaches serving high school, collegite, and professional sport teams. In mid-1980s, when it introduced its first certification—Certified Strength and Conditioning Specialist (CSCS), its influence in the industry really began to take hold. Previously, the association's primary audience was professionals working as strength and conditioning coaches. Because its CSCS certification addressed a specific need of fitness professionals in the club setting, its authority and popularity as an industry-related association emerged. NSCA subsequently developed a personal trainer certification that became very popular in the health/ fitness club industry.

Equipment Innovations and Equipment Manufacturers of the 80s

The 1980s was a revolutionary time for the equipment industry, as numerous large and small innovations in equipment and apparatus changed the face of the industry.

❑ Cardiovascular Equipment

The most ground-breaking equipment innovation of the 80s was the StairMaster 5000, originally designed and built by Lanny Potts, one of the three principals of StairMaster Exercise Systems (founded in 1983). The first StairMaster 5000, which featured rotating stairs, was introduced in 1984. Shortly after being introduced to the market, Nicholas Orlando and Randy Peterson, previously the distributors for Nautilus in the Northeast corridor of the United States approached Potts about becoming exclusive distributors of the product in the world. The two eventually purchased a significant share of the company and created Randall Sports Medical Products, which exclusively distributed the StairMaster 5000. Two years later, in 1986, Randall Sports Medical introduced the StairMaster 4000 PT mechanical stair-stepper. The 4000 PT subsequently became the most popular piece of cardiovascular equipment in the 80s and early 90s. In 1988, the company introduced another innovative product—the Gravitron, a user-friendly piece of resistance equipment that provided assistance to people who were performing dips, chin-ups, and pull-ups. The Gravitron, like the PT 4000 before it, went on to establish an entirely new category of training equipment. In doing so, both became the leading brands in their respective product categories. By 1991, the company had annual sales of approximately $45 million (equivalent to approximately $73 million in current dollars). In 1992, Randall and StairMaster merged completely to become StairMaster Sports/Medical Products, Inc. In addition to its innovative development of new equipment (e.g., PT 4000, Stepmill, Gravitron, Crossrobic machines, Spinnaker bikes, etc.), Stairmaster Sports/Medical Products, Inc. set itself apart from its competitors by focusing on three areas not directly product-related.

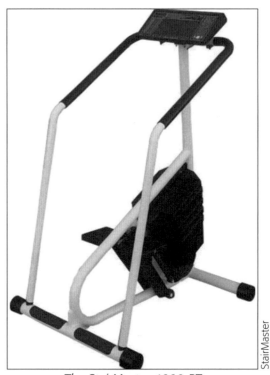

The StairMaster 4000 PT

First, they dedicated funds to research and education in fitness and medicine, thus contributing to an ever-growing body of knowledge about exercise and fitness. Second, they developed a series of workshops across the country that were designed to educate fitness professionals about exercise science and its application to the practice of fitness, rather than about their products. Finally, the company had an innovative approach to marketing, which during national trade shows, had fitness professionals waiting in relatively long lines to catch a glimpse of the corporation's new products. Some industry professionals would also claim that StairMaster was a challenging company to work with, since it never offered discounts on its products, a policy that other individuals believe helped lead to its equipment being in such high demand.

Recumbent exercise bicycles emerged in the late 1980s as an alternative to upright cycling. While recumbent outdoor bikes had been around for almost a century, their indoor cousins did not make their initial appearance in the industry until the late 1980s, mostly in response to a need for a gentler form of stationary cycling.

Schwinn IC Elite Spinning Bike

In 1987, Johnny Goldberg (Johnny G) introduced Spinning, a group-exercise program, based on the use of a special indoor bicycle. At the time his program was created, Goldberg also designed a special bicycle, which he called a Johnny G Spinner. By 1989, he had patented both his program and the bicycle. In 1995, he partnered with Schwinn to expand the reach of Spinning on a global basis.

In 1989, a small piece of accessory equipment figuratively changed the world of group exercise. This relatively small, somewhat plain, apparatus was called the "Step." The Step was developed by Gin Miller, an instructor for Sportlife, a fitness club chain in Atlanta, Georgia. The owner of Sportlife, Richard Boggs, then took the concept of Step and created the first actual mass-produced Step. Boggs then established a separate company, called the Step Company, to market and distribute the Step. Shortly thereafter, Reebok, working with Gin Miller, and two other professionals, Candice Copeland-Brooks and Lorna Francis, took the Step and developed an entire curriculum around it. Subsequently, the National Step Reebok Training Team was established.

www.ginmiller.com

Gin Miller, developer of the "Step"

❑ Resistance Equipment

During the first half of the 80s, Nautilus continued to exert its influence as the dominant equipment-related force in the industry. The name Nautilus became so synonymous with resistance machines during this time period that most resistance equipment manufacturers had a hard time establishing a foothold.

One of the most innovative lines of resistance training equipment to come to fruition in the 1980s was Hammer Strength.

One of the most innovative lines of resistance training equipment to come to fruition in the 1980s was Hammer Strength. Hammer Strength was launched in April of 1989 by Gary Jones, former director of design and engineering for Nautilus, Pete Brown, former Mid-West distributor for Nautilus and player personal director for the Cincinnati Bengals, and Kim Wood, Pete Brown's partner in the Midwest Nautilus distributorship and the strength coach for the Cincinnati Bengals. Hammer Strength machines were developed by Gary Jones, son of Nautilus founder Arthur Jones. From an engineering standpoint, the Hammer machines were different from other resistance training equipment in two distinct ways. First, the equipment utilized the principle of isolateral movement which allowed the user to train using either unilateral or bilateral movements (i.e., Hammer Strength machines enabled users to train one side or the other independently, or train them both simultaneously). Second, Hammer utilized ground-based technology that placed emphasis on using functional movements to perform the exercises. The equipment also provided a movement that closely simulated the natural strength curve of the user, similar to the variable resistance concept of Nautilus. Hammer Strength equipment initially became quite popular with strength coaches because it allowed ground-based functional movements to be performed. In fact, by the middle of the 1990s, it had become a standard piece of the fitness equipment inventory in most health/fitness club facilities. Hammer was purchased by Life Fitness in 1997.

One of the first companies to actively compete with Nautilus was Eagle Strength Systems, based in Minnesota. Eagle Strength Systems was the brainchild of Roy Simonson (the equipment's designer) and his brother, Mark. The company manufactured a very sturdy and high quality line of selectorized equipment that caught the eye of a New York-based company, Cybex, which was then a prominent maker of "physical therapy" equipment that employed isokinetic training. In 1983, Cybex purchased Eagle Strength Systems, a transaction that created the framework for what would become the Cybex company. The Cybex Eagle strength systems aggressively entered the market during the middle 1980s and, by the late 80s, had taken significant market share from Nautilus, becoming one of the top two manufacturers of resistance training equipment in the United States in the process.

In 1984, one year after Cybex Eagle entered the resistance training market, Technogym was founded in Italy. Technogym introduced its own version of selectorized variable resistance training equipment, called the Technogym Isotonic line. Because Technogym was a European based company, it focused its early efforts on the European market. Technogym grew to be the dominant manufacturer of resistance and cardiovascular equipment in Europe, and later entered the North American market.

During the 1980s, one of the trends in the industry was for smaller companies to enter the resistance training arena and manufacture "knockoffs" or alternative designs of equipment pioneered by Nautilus. Besides Cybex Eagle, Body Master and Icarian became players in the rapidly developing field of manufacturing resistance training machines.

In the late 80s, Life Fitness introduced a new category of resistance training equipment—the Life Circuit, which was an electronic line of resistance equipment. The Life Circuit allowed users to electronically program their workloads, while also providing a unique feature that enabled the equipment to remember the resistance loads exercisers used during their last workout. The Life Circuit also permitted users to design personalized programs of varying concentric and eccentric workloads. The line grew in popularity in the early 90s, but never really established a foothold in the health/fitness facility industry, ostensibly because of its being ahead of its time. Another line of electronic resistance equipment, Powercise, also made an appearance in the late 1980s. Powercise equipment was slightly different than the Life Circuit in that its machines actually communicated with the user through voice commands, becoming, in a sense, a virtual trainer of sorts. Although they had relatively advanced engineering and features, the units never caught on with the industry.

The Hammer iso-bench press machine

❏ Leading Manufacturers Founded in the 1980s

The most significant trend to emerge in the fitness equipment industry in the 80s was the establishment of companies whose influence would be a driving force in the industry for many years to come. The leading companies to emerge in the 1980s and which today command the top positions in the market include:

• Cybex International, founded in 1983, and currently one of the top manufacturers of cardiovascular and resistance training equipment in the industry

• Precor, founded in 1980, and at the present time, one of the top manufacturers of cardiovascular and resistance-training equipment in the industry and the original developer of the elliptical-training segment in the equipment industry

• Technogym, founded in 1983, and currently one of the top manufacturers of cardiovascular and resistance-training equipment in the industry, with a significant market share outside the U.S.

• Stairmaster Sports/Medical Products, Inc., founded in 1984 (formerly, Randall Sports Medical Products)—manufacturer of such well-known products as the StairMaster 5000, the PT 4000, and the Gravitron

Cybex Eagle

Cybex is currently one of the top manufacturers of cardiovascular and resistance training equipment.

Facilities of Distinction

❑   Branded Clubs Become a Rage

In 1983, Health and Tennis Corporation became Bally Health and Tennis, which subsequently was renamed as Bally Total Fitness in the 1990s. While Bally (Health and Tennis Corporation at the time) was founded in the early 1960s, it was during the 1980s that it became synonymous with the public's perception of the health/fitness club industry. During the 1980s, Bally went on an acquisition spree, purchasing numerous local and regional spa and fitness chains, which created a national chain of clubs that was over 300 strong. By 1987, Bally had became the largest health/fitness club operator in the world. Concurrent with their acquisition spree, Bally built a strong national marketing campaign that quickly established its name as the leading brand in America. Bally also caught the eye of the government because of its suspect approach to selling memberships (i.e., strong-arm tactics, high-pressure salespeople, closed doors, and non-transparent agreements). It was Bally's approach to selling memberships that helped establish IRSA as the association of quality clubs. During the 1980s, IRSA and Bally were commonly perceived by industry professionals as divergent forces. Bally and other club operators like them were responsible for specific consumer protection legislation in nearly all of the states in the U.S.

Another 800-pound gorilla in the club industry that emerged in the 1980s was 24 Hour Fitness. Founded by Mark Mastrov as a single Nautilus club in 1983, 24 Hour Fitness eventually went on to become the largest club company in the world by the beginning of the 21st century. Mastrov's concept was to establish a club that was open 24 hours a day, seven days a week. In addition, he developed a front-end management system that enabled him to later expand operations efficiently. In 1985, he brought on a partner to the organization, Leonard Schlemm. Together, the partners developed industry-leading management systems, as well as incorporated electronic funds transfer (EFT) at every club (EFT was originally introduced to the fitness industry in the 1970s). By 1994, the company became a significant player in the highly competitive Northern California market. That same year, Mastrov became one of the first industry entrepreneurs to leverage the emerging private equity market, when he partnered with private equity player McCown deLeeuw. Soon after their partnership was formed, they raised capital to purchase Ray Wilson's 72 Family Fitness Centers. This business coupling marked the beginning of a great partnership, which saw 24 Hour Fitness expand across the country through aggressive regional acquisitions and organic growth. By 2005, the company was the largest player in the world, with over 400 clubs and revenues in excess of $1 billion annually. The company was sold to private equity firm Forstmann Little & Company in 2005 for a then record $1.6 billion.

In 1989, another influential U.S. fitness company would emerge that changed the way the industry approached fitness, when Doug Levine founded

Another 800-pound gorilla in the club industry that emerged in the 1980s was 24 Hour Fitness.

a fledgling club company he called Crunch. Levine was a marketing genius who decided to develop a club he defined as "making no judgments." The first Crunch facility opened in New York and targeted a distinctly unique lower-Manhattan consumer, one who wanted a "different and irreverent" workout environment. Crunch introduced an entirely new concept to group exercise programming, offering classes such as cardio-striptease, gospel choir, drag queen, and circus. At the same time, Crunch permitted its staff to reflect the personality of its clients, quite a break from the traditional staff structure and appearance typically seen in the clubs of this decade. The most lasting contribution of Crunch was its pioneering role in the creation of a club brand. While many large companies, such as Vic Tanny, Jack LaLanne, and Bally were established earlier, it was Crunch that ushered in the era of club brands with its unique marketing approach. Crunch went beyond the four walls of its clubs, establishing a unique blend of Crunch-branded clothes, accessories, books, CDs, and videos that were sold in brick-and-mortar retail stores, and subsequently over the Internet. Crunch also had an ESPN television show. In 2001, Crunch was sold to Bally for around $90 million. Subsequently, after several years of mismanagement, the company was sold to Angelo & Gordon, a private equity group in 2005, and then re-sold in 2010 to Mark Mastrov's new investment company, New Evolution Ventures, along with various partners, including Angelo Gordon.

Another prominent club group formed in the 1980s was Sports Club/LA. Its founders, Michael Talla and Nanette Pattee Francini, originally founded the Sports Connection in 1979 and the Spectrum Clubs in 1987. It was the creation of the Sports Club/LA in Century City, California, however, that established their place in the history of the modern health/fitness club industry.

Sports Club/LA was the first club chain to introduce high-price initiation fees, costly monthly dues, and outlandish personal training prices, all of which they were able to command due to the quality experience that each Sports Club/LA facility delivered.

The first Sports Club/LA was a 100,000 square-foot club that targeted the highly affluent "ME" audience of Hollywood and Southern California. The club took on a uniquely celebrity feel, one based on a celebrity personality, featuring a narcissist atmosphere that catered to the rich and famous, as well as the aspiring rich and famous. The club offered an incredible array of dynamic and entertaining classes that were taught by celebrity instructors, as well as personal training services, physical therapy, quality dining, designer pro shops, and more. Sports Club/LA was the first club chain to introduce high-price initiation fees, costly monthly dues, and outlandish personal training prices, all of which they were able to command due to the quality experience that it delivered. Sports Club/LA opened a second club in 1989 in Irvine, California. Over the next several years, it developed several additional clubs in New York, Boston, and Washington. Currently, the two most successful of these facilities is the original club in Los Angeles and the Reebok Club in New York. Sports Club/LA, like Bally, Crunch, and 24 Hour Fitness before them, became the leading proponents of the "brand" approach to the health/fitness club industry.

Another national brand that arose in the 1980s was LA Fitness. While this chain of clubs remained a regional player in the 80s and even the 90s, by the

21st century, it became the fastest growing fitness club chain in the U.S., and by 2010, possibly the highest revenue-producing club company in the world. At its inception, LA Fitness was designed to provide a convenient low-cost workout environment that offered minimal staffing and programming, but featured a vast array of equipment.

❑ Club Leasing and Management Operators Emerge

The 1980s experienced an emergence of clubs that were built by private entrepreneurs to support large-scale commercial developments (e.g., office complexes, office and residential complexes, etc.). The developers of these large commercial complexes sought out companies to either lease the newly developed fitness spaces or to manage the on-site fitness centers on behalf of the new owners.

The first health/fitness club company to position itself to serve this new market for club management was Club Sports International (CSI), founded in 1983 by Ed Williams, Tom Lyneis, and others. Based in Denver, Colorado, CSI focused its initial efforts on providing management services for these developer-owned clubs. CSI emerged as the initial leader of this new market segment, managing high-end sports and fitness facilities in these new developments. The company established a unique market position and was sought out by numerous developers to operate clubs in their new commercial developments. CSI's brand was further strengthened by its commitment to hire highly educated staff and to feature evidenced-based fitness programs. CSI would later go on to change its name in the 1990s to Wellbridge, when it adopted a new club concept by Monsanto. By the 21st century, Wellbridge had returned to its roots, owning and operating seven high-end clubs in the Denver, Colorado market (the Colorado Athletic Clubs).

❑ The Mega-Clubs and Club Landmarks Emerge

In 1980, the East Bank Club of Chicago opened. Originally founded as an indoor tennis and racquet club, Eastbank created what could be considered the first mega-club in the industry. Occupying approximately 450,000 square feet in an old warehouse district of downtown Chicago, the East Bank Club became a role model for how a club can evolve with changing times. Over the past few decades, the club has evolved into the largest and single most profitable multipurpose club in the industry. As of 2010, the club has over 11,000 members, while generating revenues in excess of $50 million annually. The club is now a Chicago landmark and serves as a workout facility to Chicago's most prominent citizens.

During the early 1980s, another mega-club of sorts arose on the Upper East Side of New York, the Vertical Club. Occupying six floors and over 110,000 square feet, the Vertical Club quickly became the most prominent club in New York City. The rich and famous, especially celebrity personalities, all flocked to the Vertical Club, not just for its vast array of great classes and abundant

The 1980s experienced an emergence of clubs that were built by private entrepreneurs to support large-scale commercial developments (e.g., office complexes, combination office and residential complexes, etc.).

In 1982, one of the most well-known and highly respected club chains in the world was founded in the UK, David Lloyd Leisure.

equipment, but also because it was the place to be seen, and if they were lucky, the place to be found.

The Sports Club/LA discussed earlier in this chapter would also classify as one of the early mega-clubs in the industry. Clubs, such as East Bank, Chicago; the Vertical Club, NY (at least for a period of time); the Houstonian, Houston, which opened in the late 1970s; Reebok of New York, which was operated by Sports Club/LA in the early 1990s; and the Harbour Club of London, all became mega-clubs and landmarks in their respective markets. Another mega-club that originated during the 1980s was the Pro Sport Club in Bellevue, Washington, a facility that continues to thrive currently. The club occupies over 200,000 square feet and services one of the largest membership bases in the world as a result of its close relationship with Microsoft, which sponsores membeships for its employees.

International Club Brands Expand

The 1980s also experienced the continued development of the three megabrands in Asia (Central Sports, Konami Sport & Life, and Renaissance) and the evolving development of two of the other leading international club companies that were founded one to two decades earlier—Goodlife Fitness of Canada and Keiser Training AG in Germany. In 1980, Holmes Place, a leading high-end fitness club operator, opened in London. By the 1990s, Holmes Place had grown into one of the leading British operators of high-end, high-service clubs in the UK market.

In 1982, one of the most well-known and highly respected club chains in the world was founded in the UK, David Lloyd Leisure. David Lloyd was a British Davis Cup tennis player who leveraged his reputation to create what still is one of the most respected names in UK fitness. The first David Lloyd facility combined the unique elements of racquet sports (tennis and squash) with the fitness needs and social engagement of its members. Over the next decade, David Lloyd became the leading brand of fitness and racquet clubs in England. In 1995, the company created a huge sensation in the fitness industry when it was sold for a large sum of money to Whitbread, PLC, a large publically traded company. David Lloyd and Holmes Place were instrumental factors in the beginning of what would become a "British Invasion" of the global fitness market in the 1990s.

Finally, in the early 1980s, the Cannons Group was formed (the company was originally established as Archer Leisure in 1978). Cannons, founded by Harm Tegelaars, was developed as a premium health/fitness club chain, featuring multipurpose facilities. The clubs provided clients with racquet sports, gyms, pools, and crèches. By the middle of the 1990s, the Cannons Group operated approximately 17 clubs. Two industry leaders in Brazil also emerged in the 1980s—Runner, founded in 1983, and Companhia Athletic, founded in 1985.

The Slow Graying
of the Baby Boomers
(1990s)

Chapter 6

"There is good news for all Americans. Scientific evidence shows that physical activity done at a moderate-intensity level can produce health benefits. If people have been sedentary, they can improve their health and well-being with regular moderate levels of activity each day."
— Surgeon General's Report on Physical Activity and Health, 1996

Aging Baby Boomers, Technology, and Fast Money Impact the Industry Landscape

As the clock turned on the 1980s, America's baby boomers (78 million strong by census estimates) began to visualize their own mortality. By 1990, the first wave of baby boomers had recently passed the age of 40, and the balance of the post-war generation was quickly approaching that dreaded personal milestone. As baby boomers approached 40, many of them had come to the realization that their health and living a long and energetic life, more than beauty and physical prowess, was a preferred outcome of the way they lived. Coinciding with this new realization about living and health, baby boomers were in the midst of experiencing the fastest evolving period of technology development in the history of mankind, a period in which the cell phone, laptop computer, MP3s, DVDs, and video games became an integral part of almost everyone's life. Finally, in the midst of the evolving technology and the often less-than-enjoyable physical manifestations of reaching 40, many baby boomers had to deal with the new realities of Wall Street, when private equity changed the way investors looked at business. All factors considered, the 90s represented the most explosive, evolutionary period in recorded history up to that point in time. Simultaneously, the largest generation in the history of mankind was reaching a point in their biological makeup when change was not so easy for many of its members. The blending of these dynamics resulted in changes in how fitness was perceived—both from an individual and a business perspective, as well.

The most recognized influential factor in the 1990s on the fitness industry was the release in 1996 of the Surgeon General's Report on Physical Activity and Health.

Artisans and Influencers of the Decade

❑   Agencies, Associations, and Groups of Influence

The 1990s witnessed a shift in how the fitness industry was influenced. In previous decades, it was individual artisans, entrepreneurs, and innovators who had the greatest impact on how the fitness world was shaped. By 1980, while individuals continued to play a major role in affecting the fitness industry, associations and groups of individuals began to play an even more significant role. By 1990, the most influential factors bringing pressure to bear on fitness in America were driven by demographics, basic cultural issues, and groups of individuals and businesses.

The most recognized influential factor in the 1990s on the fitness industry was the release in 1996 of the Surgeon General's Report on Physical Activity and Health. The report, entitled, *Physical Activity and Health: A Report of the Surgeon General*, was a landmark publication that set forth a message that America's health woes were the result of a sedentary lifestyle. Not since a similar report released by the Surgeon General on smoking in the 1960s, had the nation's leading medical authority authored a report that disparaged America's lifestyle and its impact on the health of every American. The report sent forth a message that health conditions and diseases, such as diabetes, cancer, hypertension, heart disease, and obesity, could all be either prevented or at least minimized by engaging in moderate physical activity most days of the week. The message was simple, succinct, and powerful: Americans should accumulate at least 30 minutes of moderate-intensity physical activity most days of the week. Not only was this the directive of the Surgeon General, this message was supported by a host of professional associations, including the American Heart Association and the American College of Sports Medicine.

Leading up to the Surgeon General's report, associations, such as the American Heart Association, American College of Sports Medicine, American Arthritis Foundation, and American Cancer Society, were all disseminating information about the benefits of eating healthy and engaging in moderate-intensity physical activity on a regular basis. Science and the groups that conducted research to support its tenets had a message to share, and it was the same—Americans needed to get off their rear ends and become more physically active.

In 1992, the American College of Sports Medicine published the first edition of its landmark text, *ACSM's Health/Fitness Facility Standards and Guidelines*. This landmark document was the first effort by any group to establish standard benchmarks on how health/fitness facilities should deliver the fitness experience to consumers, setting forth standards and guidelines for practices, such as pre-activity screening, emergency procedures, staff qualifications, etc. In 1997, a second edition of this book was published, which put the industry on notice that the industry was not only about sales, but also about providing consumers with a safe, effective, and productive fitness environment. These seminal works were only a beginning. As such, other associations also began to influence how science and medicine impacted the fitness industry, and as a consequence, how the public viewed fitness.

The first edition of ACSM's landmark text, ACSM's
Health/Fitness Facility Standards and Guidelines

In the middle of the 1990s, the American Heart Association began promoting what it called public access defibrillation (PAD), a process that involved the use of a new device named an automated external defibrillator (AED). This device was designed to enable anyone (including ordinary citizens) to apply lifesaving electrical shocks to a person experiencing a life-threatening cardiac event. The introduction of the AED, as well as guidelines established for its use by the American Heart Association, permanently changed the landscape of the fitness industry. By the late 1990s, state legislatures were looking into legislation that would require health/fitness clubs to incorporate AEDs into their operating practices.

During the 1990s, certification of personal trainers became a prevalent practice, and along with it numerous certifying organizations. What was originally a small group of prominent certifying groups initially formed in the 1970s and 1980s (ACE, ACSM, AFAA, NSCA) soon grew into a major undertaking in its own right, with over 100 organizations claiming to have the personal trainer certification of choice. The rapid growth of certifying organizations had a significant impact on the landscape for the fitness industry, its operators, its trainers, and the clients who joined health/fitness club facilities.

> During this period, the International Health, Racquet, and Sportclub Association (IHRSA) began to exert far more influence on the industry than it did during its fledgling decade of the 80s.

During this period, the International Health, Racquet, and Sportclub Association (IHRSA) began to exert far more influence on the industry than it did during its fledgling decade of the 80s. Now, firmly entrenched as the primary association for the health/fitness club industry, the Association began to change under the influence of its board, particularly its executive director, John McCarthy. By the middle of the 1990s, the association had changed its name from IRSA to IHRSA, representing a fundamental shift in how it saw its role in serving the fitness facility industry. The Association was responsible for a host of publications, ranging from the benefits of exercise to facility industry benchmark data. In addition, IHRSA was establishing standards that would apply to its member clubs, lobbying state governments on important legislation impacting the industry, and expanding its reach in the global marketplace, all efforts which would fundamentally change elements of the health/fitness club industry and bring it more into the mainstream of American culture.

In the 90s, the Fitness Industry Association (FIA), the industry association for health/fitness clubs in England, was founded. Over the course of this decade, the FIA played a significant role in helping to bring the club industry to prominence in England.

❑   People of Influence

During previous decades, many of the individuals who had had the greatest impact on the fitness industry were cultural icons and self-promoters of physical culture. During the 1990s, however, the individuals who had the most influence on the fitness industry were industry insiders, people who grew up in fitness and were shaping the industry from the inside, rather than from the outside. Among the more influential of these industry insiders during the 90s were the following individuals:

- *Bahram Akradi, Chief Executive Officer of LifeTime Fitness*. As the founder and chief executive officer of Lifetime Fitness, Akradi employed a revolutionary club concept to develop Lifetime Fitness into an industry powerhouse. Akradi may well be best known for taking his company public and for his efforts to help LifeTime Fitness maintain a strong presence in the public markets, such that other companies in the fitness industry often seek out a similarly successful IPO in America.

- *Mike Balfour, Chief Executive and Founder of Fitness First, UK*. Balfour was the CEO of Fitness First when it went through rapid expansion in the first half of the 1990s. His organization was the first UK club company to float on the alternative market. Several years later, his company returned to the private sector. Balfour also helped Fitness First establish a foothold on the European mainland and later in Asia and Australia, making it the first UK club company to do so.

- *Mark Mastrov, Chief Executive Officer of 24 Hour Fitness*. As the founder of 24 Hour Fitness, Mastrov led the rapid expansion of 24 Hour Fitness during the 1990s, resulting in it becoming the industry leader by the end of the decade. Mastrov also took the lead in connecting modern-day celebrities to specific club models by creating club prototypes that featured various celebrities, such as Magic Johnson and Andre Agassi.

- *John McCarthy, Executive Director of IHRSA*. As the executive director of IHRSA, it could be validly argued that McCarthy did more than anyone else in the industry to help shape the industry, particularly IHRSA's positions on public policy, its public relations efforts, and its actions to help establish the health/fitness club industry as a mainstream industry in America.

- *Philip Mills, Founder of Les Mills International*. Mills was the originator and inspiration behind the most popular pre-packaged and choreographed group-exercise programs in the world. The company, Les Mills International, was founded in 1997, seven years after its creators had developed their first exercise program, BODYPUMP, which was initially introduced in Australia in 1995. During the next two years, Mills and his associates retained their first international distributors. By 1997, with the founding of Les Mills International, BODYPUMP was renamed and introduced to the world as a Les Mills program. By 1998, Les Mills had created four new well-received programs (BODYCOMBAT, BODYBALANCE, BODYSTEP, and RPM). In the process, the company and its founder were on their way to becoming the most recognized global name in group exercise. At the present time, Les Mills programs are offered in over 13,000 facilities around the world, making them a global fitness presence and making their CEO and founder, Philip Mills, an influential force in the global fitness marketplace.

At the present time, Les Mills programs are offered in over 13,000 facilities around the world, making them a global fitness presence and making their CEO and founder, Philip Mills, an influential force in the global fitness marketplace.

- *Augie Nieto, President of Life Fitness*. The founder and first president of Life Fitness, Nieto was a major player in shaping the industry in the 90s. His inspired leadership not only influenced the exercise equipment of the 90s, but his sponsorship of educational events and conventions, including the first ever IHRSA European Conference, helped to expand the global impact of the health/fitness facility industry.

Philip Mills, founder and CEO of Les Mills International

www.lesmills.com

Equipment Innovations and Equipment Manufacturers of the 90s

The equipment industry of the 90s acted similarly to manufacturers in other industries. The focus on this segment of the industry was more on replicating already successful pieces from other manufacturers, rather than on creating entirely new products. Nonetheless, the 90s saw the rise of several innovative new products that would change the way that many people exercised in the future.

❑ Cardiovascular Equipment

The most significant equipment innovation of the 1990s was developed by Precor, which, in 1995, introduced the world to elliptical training. In 1995, Precor introduced the EFX 544 Elliptical Trainer, which revolutionized indoor cardiovascular training for many exercisers. Up until 1995, the most popular pieces of aerobic training equipment were Lifecycles, mechanical stairclimbers (pioneered by StairMaster), and treadmills. The EFX, as it became more commonly known, established an entirely new mode of training, one based on providing a minimally impactful form of aerobic exercise. The EFX eliminated the harsh impact of running on a treadmill and the intensity and muscle discomfort that some individuals claim to have experienced while working out on a mechanical stairclimber. The EFX was the perfect fit for the energizing baby boomer generation, whose members were hitting 40. In the 90s, the EFX became what the StairMaster 4000PT was to the 80s and what Nautilus and Lifecycle were to the 70s. By helping to establish a new category of aerobic training equipment, it simultaneously became synonymous with that category. Shortly after Precor introduced the EFX 544, other manufacturers released their own versions of the elliptical trainer, using slightly different technology and different names to brand the equipment (e.g., cross-trainer, etc.).

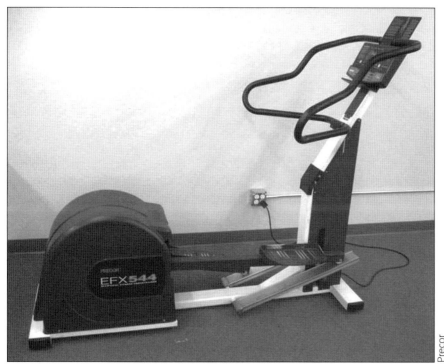

The Precor Elliptical 544

   While not a new equipment innovation, the treadmill figuratively took off in the 1990s, a circumstance that could, at least, be partially attributed to the aging baby boomer population. Several companies, such as Precor, which introduced its first commercial treadmill in 1990, Life Fitness, Star Trac, Trotter (later Cybex), and Woodway, introduced a variety of commercial treadmills to the market. By the end of the 20th century, treadmills were the most popular piece of cardiovascular equipment in health/fitness facilities. Over the 1990s, treadmills helped show the way in introducing and expanding technology into cardiovascular equipment, leading to a variety of features, such as heart rate monitoring; sophisticated workout programs; integration with hand-held devices, such as the Palm (Star Trac was the first company to introduce and incorporate the integration of its products with the Palm OS); and finally, combining newly introduced entertainment products, such as Cardio Theater, with specific exercise pieces. In the latter half of the 1990s, Technogym introduced its Key Card system that allowed users to download their workout programs from Technogym cardiovascular equipment (treadmills, bikes, stairclimbers, etc.) onto the special Technogym Key Card.

Group-cycling bikes became the rage in the early 1990s. After Johnny G introduced "Spinning" in 1989, a host of companies, including Schwinn, Reebok, Star Trac, and Life Fitness, subsequently introduced their own version of the group cycle.

In 1994, the world of virtual reality instantly impacted the fitness industry when Tectrix, a small California-based equipment manufacturer known for its quality stairclimbers and bikes (eventually purchased by Cybex), introduced the Tectrix VR bike. The Tectrix VR was a recumbent bike that incorporated several unique features that were new to cardiovascular equipment. The Tectrix bikes allowed the user to select from a variety of virtual courses, both scenic and competitive, which they could then bicycle through. The bikes not only allowed the user to select a "virtual terrain," they also permitted exercisers to actually move the bike by leaning either to the left or right. The VR never really caught on and slowly faded from the landscape, most likely because it arrived before the market was able to fully understand (and therefore adopt) it.

❏ Resistance Training Equipment

The most significant resistance training breakthrough of the 90s was the introduction of the Ground Zero functional training line of resistance equipment in 1999.

The most significant resistance training breakthrough of the 90s was the introduction of the Ground Zero functional training line of resistance equipment in 1999. The Ground Zero (its name was changed to Free Motion in late 2001) line was the brainchild of Roy Simonson, formerly the lead engineer for Cybex Eagle. The Ground Zero pieces, particularly the Cable Cross, reintroduced to both the fitness industry and to personal trainers, in particular, a method for achieving functional movement with resistance equipment. The Ground Zero equipment revolutionized the industry, given that nearly all equipment manufacturers decided to develop machines that replicated the functionality of the Ground Zero Cable Cross.

Resistance training equipment took a unique twist in 1999, when Guus van der Meer of the Netherlands officially introduced Whole Body Vibration (WBV) (i.e., acceleration training) to the public. WBV training had been around since the 1960s, when it was used by the Soviets to help condition cosmonauts in space to combat muscle and bone loss due to the effects of gravity. WBV training, which transmits waves of energy through the entire body, has been found to have a beneficial impact on the overall health of muscle tissue. The first of these machines, the Power Plate, was introduced in 1999. The company, Power Plate International Limited, which produces and distributes the Power Plate, was established in 2001.

❏ Entertainment and Technology in the 1990s

The 1990s was a decade of rapid change in technology, highlighted by the introduction of laptops, cell phones, and hand-held, personal digital assistants. The fitness industry was also impacted by this rapidly changing level of technology—changes that influenced everything from work to play.

In 1989, David Tate developed Cardio Theater—an innovative 12-channel amplifier system. Two years later, Tony DeLeede, owner of Australian Bodyworks in Atlanta, Georgia, saw the drawing power of Cardio Theater and installed the system in his clubs. Over the next few years DeLeede singly introduced the health/fitness club industry to Cardio Theater. At the time, Cardio Theater caused a revolutionary shift in the industry. It brought entertainment to the health/fitness club industry by offering facility members a means to watch television, while exercising on equipment. The first Cardio Theater system involved televisions mounted on walls or ceilings. The system had special transmitters and receivers that allowed the user to connect a special headphone into a receiving unit. This unit was attached to the cardiovascular equipment on which exercisers could choose one of several stations to watch their particular selection on a TV, while listening to it through their headset. The first Cardio Theater units employed hardwire technology and had a small range of station options. Over the years, however, the company switched to wireless transmitters and offered a broad array of viewing options. Shortly after being introduced, Cardio Theater became an essential equipment accessory for clubs. Two years after Cardio Theater burst on the scene, a second company, Broadcast Vision, introduced a distinctly different form of entertainment option that allowed facilities to provide televisions that transmitted specific station selections to unused FM frequencies. This feature allowed exercisers to use their own portable radios to tune in to a specific station, without using club assigned channels and headphones.

Cardio Theater in an Australian Bodyworks facility

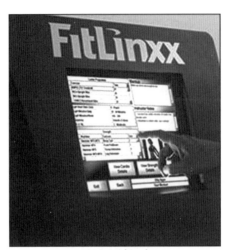

FitLinxx kiosk

In 1993, a new technology product was developed that enabled users to monitor their workouts on both resistance and cardio equipment, FitLinxx. FitLinxx incorporated a central kiosk or computer that involved having exercisers enter their core data. Each piece of equipment had a special console on which the exerciser placed a special key card that recorded their workout data, including the resistance used, repetitions, time, etc. When exercisers completed their workout, they could then download their data into the main terminal. Each time exercisers worked out, the card would serve as a virtual trainer, insuring them of knowing the specifics of their last workout, which enabled them to make necessary adjustments to their current workout, including incorporating workout progressions. FitLinxx was somewhat similar to the key card system that was developed by Technogym around the same time period. Like the Technogym system, FitLinxx never became all that popular, primarily due to its high acquisition cost to the club operator, and the relative unwillingness of consumers (or their lack of preparedness) to incorporate such technology into their daily exercise routines.

Technogym system console

In 1994, Tom Proulx and Bryan Arp introduced yet another new technology product to the fitness industry, Netpulse, which was the first Internet-based entertainment system for the health/fitness club industry. The Netpulse product consisted of a special screen/terminal that could be mounted on cardiovascular equipment and that allowed the exerciser to access the Internet and surf the emerging Web. Unfortunately, the Web was not easily accessible in those early years, as bandwidth was narrow and download speeds were slow. As a result, while the product and service was innovative, the infrastructure of the country was not sufficient to make the service easily accessible. Furthermore, the original Netpulse prototype was based on a model created by the Dot. com industry, whose underlying premise was to generate revenue through advertising subscription. When this model did not pan out, the cost for the Netpulse product increased significantly. As a consequence, the fitness industry rejected it. Netpulse temporarily disappeared as a supplier to the industry. In recent years the company has returned to the fitness industry as a provider of online media entertainment with on-demand video and audio, Web access, and related Internet-based entertainment features.

Netpulse was the first Internet-based entertainment system for the health/fitness club industry.

Toward the end of the 20th century, another company, E-zone, introduced a product that revolutionized how entertainment was presented to the users of health/fitness clubs. About 1999, it introduced its E-Zone Personal Entertainment System to the club industry. The E-Zone System allowed facility operators to provide a personal viewing screen for each piece of cardiovascular equipment. The system initially employed nine-inch viewing screens that were connected to a custom-designed frame that ran along the length of the cardiovascular equipment. In essence, the system featured a railing with individual viewing screens that were mounted in intervals along the railing in front of individual cardiovascular pieces, and were combined with special video and audio towers for transmitting content. The screens had accompanying special custom headphones that exercisers would either purchase or receive from the facility that allowed them to tune into the station they chose to watch. In addition, exercisers could wear this headset around the club and continue to either listen to the same station or tune into a radio station. The E-Zone equipment was the first of its kind to provide the exerciser with the ability to have a personal viewing screen, as well as a personal headset. The E-Zone system was not inexpensive, costing nearly one thousand dollars per viewing screen, plus the additional expense of the headsets (the pricing varied, based on the type of headset chosen). The E-Zone system became popular, and during the early part of the 21st century, was the primary form of personal viewing systems available in many clubs. One of the largest early installations of this equipment was undertaken by Town Sports International of New York, which installed over 7,000 E-Zone viewing stations in its club, starting in 2000. Shortly after the turn of the century, companies, such as Cardio Theater and Broadcast Vision, introduced less-costly personal viewing systems that featured larger screens, initially mounted on stands, and subsequently mounted on the equipment itself in later years.

Facilities of Distinction

*"Health clubs have undoubtedly been aided by a
strong economy and their own marketing ingenuity…
one benefitting from a failure of self motivation
among many fitness participants."*

— Harvey Lauer, American
Sports Data Inc., 1999

The aforementioned quote by Harvey Lauer provides an accurate summary of the forces that essentially drove the growth of the fitness industry in the 1990s. The 90s was quite possibly one of the fastest periods of growth in the fitness facility industry, with the European market (particularly the UK) experiencing a rapid evolution. According to IHRSA research, the number of health/fitness club facilities in the U.S. during the 90s increased by over 20 percent, led by an infusion of private equity, branding, and karaoke-type fitness facilities.

❏ The Era of Branded Big Boxes and Little Boxes

While large club companies had evolved in early decades (e.g., Vic Tanny, Ray Wilson's Jack LaLannne European Health Spas, and Bally), the 90s elicited a new model of branded, standardized big-box and small-box operations that would forever change the landscape of the fitness industry. These branded karaoke models also led the way in attracting private equity, thereby becoming the first club operators to bring forth highly leveraged growth. Among these pioneering club companies were the following:

> **The 90s elicited a new model of branded, standardized big-box and small-box operations that would forever change the landscape of the fitness industry.**

- *24 Hour Fitness.* Founded as 24 hour Nautilus in the 80s, it was in the mid-90s when the company received large infusions of equity capital, some of which it used to purchase Ray Wilson's Family Fitness centers. At that point, the company began to adopt a true branded and standardized big-box approach to the fitness facility business. 24 Hour Fitness created a recognizable brand by establishing a brand promise of affordability and 24-hour convenience, supported by relationships to key celebrity figures. Over the decade, 24 Hour Fitness developed several branded club types (as of 2010, they had five specific models), each carrying the 24 Hour Fitness logo. By the turn of the century, the company had become 24 Hour Fitness Worldwide, with holdings in America, Asia, and Europe. Over the course of the 90s, 24 Hour Fitness was able to attract considerable private equity.
- *LifeTime Fitness.* Founded in 1990 by Bahram Akradi, Lifetime established a new brand and business model for the fitness industry, opening its first club in 1992. Lifetime Fitness would quickly become the Best Buy or Target of fitness, creating a standardized "big-box" model that could be easily and successfully replicated by them. Lifetime Fitness developed a brand promise, built around large full-service facilities (typically over 100,000 square feet), designed to service the needs of an entire family at an affordable price. The company introduced a number of well-received attractions, including

large kid's clubs, indoor pools with water slides, enormous fitness floors with over 300 pieces of equipment, and facilities that looked the same, no matter where you lived. Over the decade of the 90s (the company officially became LifeTime, Inc. in 1998), LifeTime Fitness became an industry sensation, which enabled it to go public in 2001. As such, LifeTime Fitness changed the suburban landscape for club operators by introducing and mastering a standardized approach to big-box family fitness that delivered excellent value at an affordable price.

A LifeTime Fitness facility

The cardiovascular area in a 24 Hour Fitness facility in San Ramon, California

Equinox fitness clubs target young, well-educated, and well-paid urban professionals.

- *Equinox Fitness*. Opening its first club on the Upper West Side of Manhattan around 1992, Equinox subsequently evolved into a premium brand by the end of the decade. The first Equinox club established a brand promise by offering a "sexy and appealing facility" that featured a large variety of dynamic and innovative group-classes, combined with top-level personal trainers. Equinox was also one of the first facilities to target a specific demographic audience, when it targeted young, well-educated, and well-paid urban professionals. During the 90s, under the leadership of its original owners, subsequently under the direction of its equity investors, Equinox created a standardized business model around its technology, programs, and people, a model that could be replicated in other urban environments. The company initially emerged as a powerhouse in New York. By the end of the decade, however, it had moved to other large urban markets (Chicago, Los Angeles, San Francisco, etc.) that were populated by young, hip, urban professionals.

- *Crunch*. Founded by Doug Levine in 1989, the 90s made Crunch a household name in the fitness industry. As was detailed in Chapter Four, Crunch established a brand promise that served a distinctly unique lower Manhattan consumer, an individual who wanted a "different and irreverent" workout environment. It was Crunch that ushered in the era of club brands, with its unique marketing approach. Crunch went beyond the four walls of its clubs, establishing a unique blend of Crunch-branded clothes, books, videos and accessories sold in stores, and subsequently over the Internet. Interestingly, while Crunch established a great brand, equal to if not more powerful than the other of those brands discussed in this chapter, what Crunch did not develop was a big-box mass market. Rather, Crunch created a highly specialized niche brand.

- *LA Fitness International*. While LA Fitness was actually founded in 1984, it remained a relatively small Southern California operation until 1995. By then, the company had developed a prototype club that would go on to become the template for one of the largest branded "big-box" operators in the world. The LA Fitness brand was similar, in many ways, to several of the older club business models, such as Bally, especially with regard to its sales model. The LA Fitness brand promised large, convenient, and accessible facilities and equipment, both at a very affordable price. The LA Fitness model eliminated waste, providing a limited level of staffing and programming. Instead, it offered access and convenience at an incredibly favorable price point. By the late 90s, the company had well over a dozen clubs. More recently, it has expanded to over 300 facilities. Like many operators who opened or grew rapidly during this period, LA Fitness did an exceptional job of attracting private equity.

It should be noted that during the 90s, a number of recognizable and successful club companies, in addition to those already discussed in this chapter, were established. As such, several club companies, such as Planet Fitness, Gold's Gym, World Gym, Town Sports International, and Spectrum Clubs, developed distinct brand promises and scalable and standardized operating models.

LA Fitness clubs are designed to offer large, convenient, and accessible facilities and equipment, at a very affordable price.

❑ Niche Players in Emerging New Markets

The 90s, while dominated by the well-oiled, big-box and small-box club companies, was also a period that experienced the introduction or re-invention of new club models. Among the more unique of these niche models were the following:

- *Curves*. Curves was founded in 1992 by Gary and Diane Heavin, in Harlington, Texas. Curves introduced the fitness facility industry to the power and financial potential of creating a highly branded niche club model. Curves pioneered the concept of a 30-minute express facility that catered to the needs of a niche audience—in this instance, deconditioned women. The Curves model provided a small, intimate, non-intimidating setting that offered women a structured 30-minute workout comprised of both resistance training and cardiovascular activity. The tagline of "no make-up and no men" became the calling card of the brand, which allowed it to penetrate an entirely new demographic that other fitness facilities had previously been unable to capture. In 1995, Curves opened its first franchised facility, in Paris, Texas. A decade later, Curves had opened over 7,000 franchised clubs, making it the fastest growing franchise operation in the world. The success of Curves can be attributed not only to its ability to develop a brand that appealed to the social, emotional, and physical needs of a relatively untapped population of adults who wished to exercise (e.g., women who typically were slightly overweight and over 30), but also to its franchise model, which enabled entrepreneurs to start a business with low capital entry. The Curves franchise allowed facilities to be developed in as little as 300 square feet, a feature that permitted entrepreneurs to open sites in strip malls, residential developments, and commercial developments at relatively minimal cost.

© Richard Graulich/Palm Beach Post/ZUMA Press

The Curves model provided a small, intimate, non-intimidating setting that offered women a structured 30-minute workout comprised of both resistance training and cardiovascular activity.

- *Exhale Spas*. Exhale was founded by Annbeth Eschbach at the end of the decade. The Exhale concept was entirely new to the industry. The Exhale brand promise was built around merging mind and body health. Exhale Mind Body Spas combined a high-end spa experience with state-of-the-art program elements that focused on healing, the core, and yoga. The Exhale facilities feature spa treatment rooms, as well as studios that offer custom classes in yoga, and core fusion programs designed around both the renowned Lotte Berk method and the ever-popular Pilates. The Exhale Spas did not sell memberships. Rather, they offered individual and packed programs around their classes, spa treatments, and healing services. The clubs targeted an upscale, professional, and baby-boomer market of women primarily, living in dense urban markets. After a decade of operation, Exhale Spas had over 18 facilities throughout the U.S.

- *Medical Fitness Facilities*. While hospital-based fitness facilities emerged in the late 1970s with the opening of the Integris Health PACER fitness Center, it was not till the 1990s that this segment of the fitness industry really took off. As baby boomers started their slow, but steady, decent into middle age, and as healthcare costs increased nationally, a need arose for a medically based model of fitness delivery. During the 90s, over 500 hospitals in the U.S. incorporated fitness into their business model. Their focus was two-fold. The first aim was to create a health-prevention facility where individuals with underlying health risks could safely and effectively engage in a fitness regimen under the guidance of qualified fitness professionals, supported by healthcare professionals. The second objective was to provide an environment, referred to as secondary rehabilitation or post-rehabilitation. In the 1990s, healthcare insurers had reduced support for a number of services, such as cardiac rehabilitation and physical therapy, resulting in numerous individuals being left without proper professional guidance in their efforts to recover from medical conditions that were previously the sole purvey of physical therapists and related medical professionals. This shift in healthcare dynamics drove the market for post-rehabilitative services, which created the demand, along with preventative medicine through exercise, for medically based fitness facilities. Eventually, the ever-expanding medical fitness market resulted in the establishment of the Medical Fitness Association. As of 2010, over 1,100 medically based fitness centers are in the U.S. alone.

International Clubs Gain Prominence

While the U.S. remained the leading fitness facility market in the world, the international market, which had grown slowly during previous decades, began to exert significant influence in the fitness industry—locally, regionally, and globally. While U.S. operations were competing for similar market share in many cases, the international markets were relatively virgin territory. It was in the 1990s that countires such as Argentina, Chile, China, India, and Russia experienced an emergence and then a rapid evolution of health and fitness clubs. The nation that demonstrated the most significant growth during this period was England.

❏ British Clubs Take Front and Center

The British market in the 90s, in many ways, resembled the U.S. market of the 80s, with phenomenal growth in both clubs and business models. One of the more interesting developments that occurred in the British market during this period was the rapid introduction of private equity and, subsequently, the floating of public offerings. Interestingly, the British market, more than the U.S. market, became the model for IPOs in the health/fitness club segment during the 1990s. Among the more prominent British club companies during this time period (all of which continued to play a leading role in the British health/fitness club market in 2010) were the following:

> The British market in the 90s, in many ways, resembled the U.S. market of the 80s, with phenomenal growth in both clubs and business models.

- *Fitness First*. Fitness First was founded by Mike Balfour in 1993. Fitness First developed a unique and successful brand, built around the promise of affordable and convenient fitness for the masses. The first Fitness First clubs featured a facility of approximately 15,000 to 20,000 square feet (1,500 to 2,000 meters) that had a gym, changing areas, a group studio, and a children's crèche. One of the factors that differentiated the brand from other clubs was video rentals, which allowed members to actually select and rent videos from the Fitness First clubs. Fitness First was able to identify locations throughout London and other regions of England where the company could develop space inexpensively and then lease it at a very reasonable rate. Fitness First's growth was so rapid during its first several years that it became the first British club company to float on the alternative market. In 1998, Fitness First was also the first British company to enter mainland European markets, and later in both Asia and Australia. At the present time, Fitness First has more clubs in more global markets than any other company in the health/fitness club industry. It is also one of the two highest revenue-generating fitness club companies in the world.
- *David Lloyd Leisure*. Founded in 1982, David Lloyd Leisure rose to prominence in the 1990s by positioning itself as a premium multipurpose operator that offered racquet sports, fitness, and a social environment. David Lloyd also created a sensation in the mid-90s (1995 to be exact), when it was sold to Whitbread PLC, a transaction that provided it with access to capital that would allow it to prosper during the 90s.

- *LA Fitness.* Founded in 1990 by Fred Turok and Jeremy Taylor, this company, which should not be confused with the U.S. firm of the same name, began its rise to prominence during the same decade. The original clubs, managed by Turok and his partner, were not officially called LA Fitness until 1996. The LA Fitness model focused on delivering a reasonably priced club environment that offered a fun, engaging, and social fitness experience to its target audience. By 1999, LA Fitness was listed on the London stock exchange. The company would later return to the private sector, where it would subsequently grow into a company with over 40 clubs.

- *Esporta.* Esporta was founded in 1994. This chain of clubs targeted an upscale audience of adults and families by offering comprehensive facilities, engaging programs, and an exceptional staff. At the turn of the century, the company floated on the London Stock Exchange. Within two years, however, it was taken private again. The company operates over 40 premium clubs throughout England.

❑ A German Company Sets the Stage for a New 21st Century Fitness Club Model

In 1997, Rainer Schaller founded McFit, in Germany. At the time of its creation, McFit was just a new club on the market. Ten years later, however, the company had become a role model of sorts for how to operate and market a highly successful economy-club business model (commonly referred to as high volume – low price). Schaller's club model was based on delivering a convenient, user-friendly, no frills, and extremely affordable club model to the masses. To bring his dream to life, Schaller created a new club model that featured:

Rainer Schaller, founder of McFit—the prototype for delivering no-frills, affordable fitness to the masses

- Large gym (the European name for a fitness center), with lots of equipment (no group studios)
- Limited staffing (typically one staff member is on duty at all times who works reception, sells memberships, and provides assistance to members)
- High-tech instruction and communication (in-club computer kiosks allow members to receive professional instruction and relevant information regarding exercise and nutrition, as well as the opportunity to read articles, view the company's magazine, etc.)
- No-frills amenities (e.g., members have to pay to use a shower; the facilities do not provide towels or offer group classes; only key-card access is available during off-hours, etc.)

McFit's motto, "Ein fach gut aussehen" or "simply look good," has become the calling card for this highly successful low-cost club model. The McFit model has become the prototype in the 21st century for delivering no-frills, affordable fitness to the masses.

❏   Other Emerging Global Brands

As stated earlier, the 1990s represented a period of rapid growth for international club operators, with many of the top global brands either forming or coming to prominence during this period. Among the most recognizable global brands to emerge during the 90s were the following:

- Fitness DK, Denmark. Originally founded in 1987, the company went through considerable growth in the 90s and today is the largest operator in Denmark.
- Gimnasio Pacific, Chile. Founded in 1995, the company currently operates over 30 clubs in Chile, making it a leading player in the Chilean marketplace..
- Megatlon, Argentina. Founded in 1995, the company currently operates over 17 clubs in Argentina, making it a leading brand of health/fitness club facilities in Argentina.
- Organizacion Britania, Mexico. Originally founded in 1975, the company currently operates over 50 clubs in Mexico and is the leading club brand in Mexico.
- Planeta Fitness, Russia. Founded in 1997 and currently the second largest club operator in Russia
- SATS, Sweden. Created in 1995, the company is the largest operator in Sweden.
- Strata Partners, Russia. Founded in 1999 and currently the third largest operator in Russia
- World Class (aka Russian Fitness Group). Founded in 1993 and currently the largest operator of clubs in Russia

> The McFit model has become the prototype in the 21st century for delivering no-frills, affordable fitness to the masses.

The Clash of Generations—Fitness in the 21st Century
(2000 to 2010)

Chapter 7

"Our business in life is not to get ahead of others, but to get ahead of ourselves—to break our own records, to outstrip our yesterdays by our today, to do our work with more force than ever before."
— Stewart B. Johnson

A Decade of Ups, Downs, and Change

The first decade of the 21st century had more than its share of consequential events. The decade began with the nation engulfed by efforts to recover from the Dot.Com bust of the late 1990s. Shortly thereafter, the worst act of terrorism on American soil occurred. The decade ended with the worst recession since the Great Depression. Sandwiched between these great upheavals were numerous wars, environmental disasters, a flattening of the global marketplace, the emergence of the BRIC (Brazil, Russia, India, and China) and their influence on the global marketplace, the lightening speed change of technology, viral celebrity and fame, and finally the great rise and fall of narcissist capitalism and overleveraged economic growth. Unquestionably, the first decade of the 21st century was one of the most complex periods in the history of the world.

One factor that is often overlooked when analyzing the first decade of the 21st century is the far-reaching shift in America's and the world's demographic make-up. During this 10-year period, baby boomers reached 50, and in some cases 60, bringing mortality and healthcare issues to the forefront of global politics and economics. Concurrently, almost 77 million echo boomers or millenials born after 1981 and the children of the baby boomers reached their late teens and early adulthood, resulting in a situation where their influence on world economies and politics became nearly as influential as that of their heralded forerunners—the baby boomers.

Artisans and Influencers of Fitness

Throughout the 19th and 20th centuries, the history of fitness was impacted by individuals and groups of individuals whose personalities, sense of entrepreneurship, and level of self-promotional acumen had put them in position to significantly influence the course of events. Whether it was the introduction of a new piece of equipment (e.g., Arthur Jones, Wayne Quinton, Augie Nieto), a new exercise regimen (e.g., Eugen Sandow, Charles Atlas, Kenneth Cooper, Jackie Sorenson), or merely spreading the gospel of exercise and health (e.g., Bernarr Macfadden, Jack LaLanne, Richard Simmons, Jane Fonda), the fitness industry was heavily, if not entirely, swayed by a host of dynamic personalities. In reality, by the 1990s, fitness had begun to move away from being influenced by a few individuals. Instead, conditions were evolving for the industry. "Pop" culture and associations of professionals (e.g., AHA, ACSM, IHRSA, etc.) were becoming the new change-agents. With the arrival of the 21st century, however, almost everything changed.

The most powerful influence on the fitness industry (including almost everything else in society) during the first decade of the 21st century was the Internet.

❑   The Internet

The most powerful influence on the fitness industry (including almost everything else in society) during the first decade of the 21st century was the Internet. Facebook, YouTube, Twitter, company websites, professional blogs, non-professional blogs, on-line educational mediums, and the impact of "buzz" or viral marketing by millions of social media users were the most compelling factors affecting the world of fitness during this period. Crossfit, Les Mills, Zumba, pole dancing, functional training, McFit, Cardio Striptease, and Mixed Martial Arts are all by-products and outgrowths of the power of the Web. The ability of the worldwide Web to impact the attitudes, beliefs, and behaviors of individuals is virtually boundless. Consumers and fitness professionals, alike, have instant access to thousands of websites to learn about a new methodology of fitness, a new exercise program, or a new scientific study detailing some aspect of health, wellness, or fitness. Possibly more importantly, the Web enables individuals to tap into sites, such as YouTube, Facebook, or Twitter, to learn what their friends and others are experiencing fitness-wise.

While Kenneth Cooper had to write a book and give speeches when he introduced the world of fitness to *"Aerobics,"* Greg Glassman only had to post his new method of training, called Crossfit (actually, the procedure is over 100 years old), on the Internet to achieve similar results. In fact, the power of social networking made Glassman's program an instant sensation. In the past, club giants, such as 24 Hour Fitness and Bally, had to spend millions to promote their brand message on TV, on radio, and in print media. In the 21st century, McFit generates most of its buzz through member-generated videos on YouTube.

In today's world, an idea can spread to hundreds of millions of individuals in seconds.

One of the most successful promotional videos for a club was developed by Leo Sports Club, an effort that thrived because of its high visibility on YouTube. Individuals who want to know about the latest research on exercise and its impact on health in previous decades would have been required to attend conventions and/or subscribe to a variety of scientific journals. In today's world, however, they can click on a host of websites, some operated by professional associations, such as ACE or ACSM, or if they're more inclined, they can connect to one of the thousands of fitness blogs. In today's world, an idea can spread to hundreds of millions of individuals in seconds. As such, fitness has come under the heavy influence of the virtual world, which in turn, is impacted not so much by one individual, but by a host of socially connected "friends."

❑   Associations and Groups of Influence

In addition to the Internet, associations continue to play an important role in how the fitness industry evolves. "Exercise is Medicine," a compelling initiative that advocates the connection between exercise and preventative and rehabilitative medicine, is substantially, if not entirely, being driven by a few key associations, such as the American College of Sports Medicine, the American Medical Association, and the American Heart Association. Through these associations and their professional networks, both fitness professionals and potential fitness consumers are learning of the meaningful impact that exercise can have on the healthcare continuum.

The International Health, Racquet, and Sportclub Association (IHRSA) in the U.S. and the European Health Fitness Association (EHFA) in Belgium are both heavily involved in public policy efforts that directly and indirectly impact the health and fitness facility industry, as well as consumer perspectives on the industry. For example, in 2006, IHRSA developed a position paper regarding the certification of personal trainers that has since become the benchmark in the industry with regard to what personal trainer certifications are appropriate for a trainer for a health/fitness club. EHFA has recently (2010) updated its standards for fitness instructors, group-exercise instructors, and trainers—standards that will impact the training and qualifications of fitness professionals throughout Europe.

Another prime example of how associations have impacted the fitness industry during the first decade of the 21st century has been the efforts of the American College of Sports Medicine, which in 2006 developed the third edition of its *ACSM Health/Fitness Facility Standards and Guidelines*. This publication established an industry standard for public access defibrillation in clubs. As a result, what was once a somewhat open-ended factor in the minds of most club operators is now firmly a part of their operating practices.

Recently, NSF International, a global safety certifying group, has spearheaded an initiative working with ACSM, IHRSA, the Medical Fitness Association (MFA), and other groups to create a global certification process for health/fitness clubs. In fact, the efforts of associations that impact the fitness industry continue to grow in both amount and scope. For example, a number of professional certification organizations, such as ACE and ACSM, are actively promoting specialty certifications for professionals who are working with individuals who have unique physical or medical conditions (e.g., cancer, disabilities, etc.). As a result, many fitness professionals are targeting new groups to help. Consumers, who once did not have an alternative for professional guidance concerning exercise, now have a means to obtain such assistance. All evidence indicates that more than ever in the past, fitness professionals and consumers are reaching out to professional trade associations to obtain needed information, rather than rely on a single individual or publication.

> All evidence indicates that more than ever in the past, fitness professionals and consumers are reaching out to professional trade associations to obtain needed information, rather than rely on a single individual or publication.

❑ Individuals of Influence

The first decade of the 21st century has not been without celebrities in the fitness industry. Among the more well-known of these individuals (each of whom has had an impact on the trends and practices during the decade) are the following:

- *Juan Carlos Santana*. Founder of the Institute of Human Performance in Florida, Santana is one of the most respected professionals in the industry, as well as a renowned expert in both functional training and personal training. He also serves as a trainer and advisor to many high-profile athletes.

- *Philip Mills*. CEO of Les Mills International, Mills developed several highly popular group-exercise programs that are a dominant force on the group-exercise landscape. As such, Mills' influence on the fitness industry is quite substantial.

- *Mark Mastrov*. Founder of 24 Hour Fitness and founder and CEO of New Evolution Ventures (owners of Crunch, Ultimate Fighting Gyms (UFC) , and Hard Candy Gyms, and an investor in numerous international club groups), Mastrov has been and continues to be a major force in the development of clubs throughout the world.

Innovative Equipment and Equipment Manufacturers of the New Decade

Interestingly, while the world has changed significantly over the first decade of the 21st century, with technology leading the way, the equipment sector has chosen to incorporate subtle changes in its menu of offerings, rather than launch any revolutionary or industry-changing innovations. In most instances, the industry has simply opted for one of three distinct approaches: bring back traditional pieces of equipment with a new twist, modify existing categories of equipment, or upgrade existing technology with new technology.

❑   Cardiovascular Equipment

In 2005, Technogym introduced Cardiowave, the first innovative piece of cardiovascular equipment to be brought to market in the 21st century. The Cardiowave, similar to the Nautilus Skate that was introduced in the 1990s, simulates the general biomechanics of blading (e.g., inline skating) or ice skating, which places emphasis on the use of the hip abductors, leg extensors, and leg rotators. The Cardiowave provides users a modality that can be used to develop cardiovascular conditioning, as well as musculoskeletal conditioning of the lower body. One apparent drawback to the equipment involves the intensity of the workout it provides, which can exceed the limits that would be typically tolerated by a first-time user.

A Cardiowave machine

The Krankcycle, developed by Johnny G

In 2007, Precor introduced the AMT100i, the Adaptive Motion Trainer to the marketplace. The AMT, as it is more commonly referred to in the industry, features "continuous variable stride length," a unique innovation that enables users to vary the length of their stride while exercising on the equipment. In addition, the equipment allows both forward and backward movements. One of the features that differentiates the AMT from other cardiovascular products is its ability to simulate elliptical training, mechanical stair-stepping, and even jogging, which basically makes it a machine that offers three distinct modalities of cardiovascular training.

In 2007, Johnny G, the original inventor of Spinning, introduced a new form of group exercise he called Kranking. Along with it, Johnny G developed a new piece of training equipment that he named the Krankcycle. It was not until the spring of 2008, when Johnny G partnered with Matrix (an industry-leading manufacturer of fitness equipment) that the Krankcycle and Kranking really took off. In reality, the Krankcycle was not a new piece of equipment, rather it was a modification of the traditional upper-body ergometers manufactured and sold by several companies, such as Cybex and Scifit.

Other than the three aforementioned pieces of equipment, the primary focus of the industry over the first 10 years of the 21st century has been to bring new technologies to old equipment, particularly in the area of entertainment. Companies, such as Life Fitness, Star Trac, and Technogym, have led the way in introducing HDLCD screens to cardiovascular equipment, as well as touch-screen technology, iPod compatibility, downloadable programming, and Internet interfaces. Currently, when individuials purchase a high-end treadmill or other cardiovascular piece from these manufacturers, they can expect to be able to connect their iPod; select exercise program and entertainment options using touch screen technology; and download their workout onto a flash drive or upload their workout to a website, where they can subsequently download the results of their workout and review them. Today, exercisers can even send email and text from their cardiovascular equipment.

❑ Resistance Training Equipment

The first decade of the 21st century experienced very little in the way of new and innovative equipment. In 2005, Technogym introduced its Kinesis Circuit, a customized line of specialty resistance equipment involving four separate modules that enables users to perform up to 250 different exercises and 400 functional movements. The Kinesis Circuit utilizes a special arrangement of pulleys and cords to simulate various functional movements. In 2008, Technogym introduced the Kinesis One, which was a single-station version of the Circuit. The Kinesis One allows exercisers to perform nearly all of the 400 movements that could be performed on the original Kinesis Circuit.

Whole Body Vibration (WBV)—acceleration, training—and the corresponding equipment used for this particular training began to gain in popularity around 2001, approximately two years after it was first introduced to the market. The first commercial piece of WBV equipment was the Power Plate. WBV initially gained widespread acceptance in the European market, especially in England and later in Germany. The U.S. market has yet to accept either the equipment or the programming on a scale that exists in Europe or other foreign markets, such as Brazil or Asia.

The first decade of the new century also witnessed a reintroduction of the equipment that was first used by physical-culture specialists nearly 150 years earlier. As the concept and acceptance of functional training and sports performance training took off during this period, so did the inclusion of training apparatus used by exercise enthusiasts and professionals more than 150 years ago. Much of the appartus used in the 1800s, including kettlebells, medicine balls, rings, ladders, sand bags, ropes, and peg boards, came back in style during this decade.

Training on a Power Plate machine

TRX Suspension Training equipment is another kind of apparatus that has gained popularity during the first decade of the 21st century. Produced and sold by Fitness Anywhere and developed by Randy Hetrick during his tenure as a Navy Seal, the TRX system allows exercisers to perform bodyweight movements, using specially designed harnesses, nylon belts, and suspension pieces. The equipment is designed to be completely portable. It also allows the equipment to be attached to a fixed wall, bar, or other sturdy structure. The movements performed with the equipment incorporate the exerciser's own bodyweight as resistance. Interestingly, the TRX Suspension Training movements and equipment reflect a close resemblance to equipment used by Eugen Sandow and other strongmen of the late 19th century.

TRX Suspension Training equipment

Fitnessanywhere.com

❑ A New Genre of Exercise Equipment—Exergaming

Exergaming and exergaming equipment became part of the lexicon of fitness at the beginning of the 21st century. As fitness professionals and physical educators looked for a means to attract young echo boomers to fitness, many of these individuals adopted principles that had been established by many of the video game companies. As a result, they incorporated physical movement into the playing of games, a practice which, in essence, created a form of virtual fitness. The underlying principle of exergaming and the equipment that it employs is based on incorporating fitness into the gaming experiencing in such a fashion that the participant does not associate the activity with exercise, but rather with gaming. The most popular and successful of these efforts was Konami's Dance Dance Revolution (DDR), which was originally introduced in game arcades years earlier. By 2005, DDR had become the most popular form of exergaming equipment in the club industry. Many clubs typically incorporate the equipment as part of a kid's area or young adult area.

> Exergaming and exergaming equipment became part of the lexicon of fitness at the beginning of the 21st century.

In addition to DDR and modifications of it that were developed by other companies, exergame consoles, such as the Cybex Trazer, which was brought to the market in 2005, and Motivatrix's MX7 Workout Master, which was also introduced in 2005, entered the exergaming market. Possibly the most successful piece of exergaming equipment to be developed during this period was the Nintendo Wii Fit system. This system was originally designed for the home market, but has since been incorporated into the fitness repertoire of many facilities. The leading company in this niche is Exergame Fitness, which distributes and sells exergaming systems to the club market by incorporating it with existing equipment produced by a variety of manufacturers. Examples of the pieces that Exergame Fitness incorporates into their comprehensive club systems include:

- Wii Fit
- Cateye upright and recumbent GameBike Pro
- Expresso recumbent bike
- Motivatrix MX10
- DDR (multiple versions)
- Brainbike

Facilities of Distinction

As the 20th century came to an end, and the 21st century began, the health/fitness facility industry saw equity markets become more enamored with the industry, driven by a combination of factors, including the predictable level of cash flow generated by the business; evidence-based research showing an increasingly unhealthy global population suffering from a variety of diseases associated with a sedentary lifestyle; a world population where less than five percent of the world's inhabitants use health clubs; and an aging baby boomer population, seeking alternatives to what they perceive as a decaying healthcare

Dance Dance Revolution (DDR) exergaming equipment

system. This unique combination of changing demographics, a pandemic of obesity, the explosion of diseases attributed to sedentary living and lifestyle, easily available capital, predictable cash flows, and a perception of a huge demand and limited supply drove the health/fitness facility industry to strong growth during the first six to seven years of the new century.

In the U.S. alone, the number of clubs grew from just over 15,000 at the beginning of the decade to over 30,000 by the end of the decade, and the number of members grew from approximately 32 million to over 46 million (it should be noted that from 2007 to 2010, growth in the number of clubs and members remained relatively flat). This growth in members and facilities was not limited to the U.S. Expansion in the international markets actually exceeded the growth experienced in the U.S. market. In fact, by the end of the decade, the U.S. market, which at one time comprised over 50 percent of the global market, only accounts for 25 percent of health/fitness facilities worldwide. Three elements in particular, helped fuel the incredible level of growth in the fitness industry—the infusion of equity capital into the industry; the growth of franchises; and the emergence of new business models.

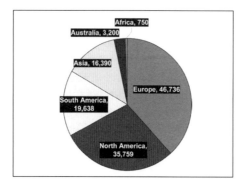 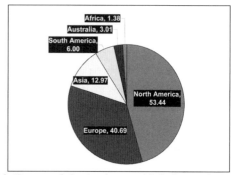

As of 2010, there were over 122,000 health/fitness clubs in the world (left graphic), which had over 117 million members (right graphic).

❏   Private and Public Capital Cascades Into the Industry

The first decade of the 21st century will also be remembered for the enormous flow of equity and debt into the fitness industry. Companies, such as Fitness First, LifeTime Fitness, LA Fitness, Urban Active Fitness, 24 Hour Fitness, Equinox, Town Sports International, Spectrum Clubs, and Lifestyle Family Fitness—to name only a few, all benefited from the surge of private capital into the industry. Some of the most prominent examples of private equity's impact on the growth of the industry during this particular period include:

- *24 Hour Fitness, San Ramon, California.* While 24 Hour Fitness came into existence in the 1980s and established a name for itself in the 90s, it was during the first five years of the 21st century that 24 Hour Fitness evolved into the largest such organization in the industry, driven by several rounds of equity infusion supported by debt. During this five-year period, McCown deLeeuw, a private equity fund that held a significant stake in 24 Hour Fitness, was able to attract approximately $500 million in debt to support both the rapid organic development of the company and a series of acquisitions that allowed 24 Hour Fitness to attain a total of 345 clubs and achieve annual revenues of $1.1 billion by 2005. In the summer of 2005, McCown deLeeuw & Company put 24 Hour Fitness up for auction, which led to Fortsmann Little and Company, a New York-based private equity fund, offering $1.6 billion to acquire the company. Fortsmann paid for the acquisition through a combination of $900 million in equity and subordinated debt funds and $700 million from a senior loan facility.

- *Equinox Holdings, New York, New York.* In 2000, North Castle Partners and J.W. Childs and Associates purchased Equinox, then an 11-club chain that generated approximately $63 million in annual revenues. Over the next five years, Equinox grew to 33 clubs in five major markets (NY, Chicago, Los Angeles, San Francisco, and South Florida). In 2003, with reported YE revenues of $116 million, the company already had debt of $163 million. By 2005, Equinox, which then had 33 clubs (not all operating), had

Private equity had a significant impact on the health/fitness club industry during the first decade of the 21st century.

reported annual revenues of $168 million, and was sold to the Related Companies, L.P., a New York real estate development firm that specialized in building high-end residential properties with prestigious addresses. Related Companies paid $505 million for Equinox.

- *Fitness First, London, England.* Fitness First emerged on the club market in the 1990s. The company actually floated on the alternative markets for a short time, before going back to being privately held by Cinven Limited at the beginning of the decade. Cinven, a private equity fund, provided capital that enabled Fitness First to grow through a combination of multiple acquisitions and organic growth. By 2005, Fitness First had 424 clubs in 15 countries, annual revenues of 590 million euros, and a reported EBITDA of 140 million euros. In 2005, BC Partners acquired Fitness First for an enterprise value of 1.2 billion euros.

In each of the aforementioned examples, the companies were able to attract significant multiples at the time of sale, not to mention take on significant levels of debt. These conditions played a significant role in the ability of these organizations to grow so rapidly through acquisitions and organic growth. In these examples, the companies were able to achieve multiples that were anywhere from 25 to 100 percent higher than those seen prior to the turn of the century. Furthermore, the level of debt carried by these companies was also higher than would have been considered acceptable a decade earlier.

It should be noted that on the downside of this infusion of highly leveraged debt and private equity were club companies that were unable to sustain the necessary growth to cover the cost of this capital. Two examples of companies that succumbed to the downside of private equity and excessive debt were Bally and Crunch.

- *Bally Total Fitness, Chicago, Illinois.* Once the largest company in the fitness club industry, Bally filed for Chapter 11 Bankruptcy twice during the decade—initially, in July of 2007, when they had reported debt of $761 million and only $397 million in assets, and again 15 months later, in December of 2008, when they filed their second Chapter 11 Bankruptcy, showing $1.5 billion in debt and $1.4 billion in assets. After the first filing, Bally reemerged two months later, having received approximately $233 million from the hedge fund Harbinger Capital. Approximately 15 months later, however, they had to file for bankruptcy a second time.
- *Crunch, New York, New York.* Originally founded in 1989, Crunch experienced celebrity status during the 1990s and, by the beginning of the 21st century, was sold to Bally Total Fitness for approximately $90 million. Several years later, Crunch was sold to Angelo, Gordon and Company for $45 million, a net loss to Bally of $45 million. In May of 2009, Crunch filed for Chapter 11 Bankruptcy, reporting debts of $57 million and assets of $22.7 million. Angelo, Gordon and Company, along with private equity fund New Evolution Ventures (owned by Mark Mastrov) and others, subsequently purchased the assets of Crunch for $20 million.

One downside of the infusion of highly leveraged debt and private equity were club companies that were unable to sustain the necessary growth to cover the cost of this capital.

A final footnote to this decade of leveraged capital involves the initial public offerings (IPOs) of two relatively large industry players in the U.S.—LifeTime Fitness and Town Sports International. IPOs are a more established method of generating capital (compared to private equity and leveraged debt), either for paying down existing debt, cashing out existing shareholders, or securing funds for future growth. In the case of both companies, the reason for the IPOs differed, as did the outcomes of the transactions, both at closing and years later.

- *LifeTime Fitness, Minnesota*. LifeTime made its initial IPO offering in the summer of 2004, offering 9.9 million shares at a price of $18.50 per share (total offering of $183,200,000). At the end of the first day, LifeTime stock closed at $21 a share and sold 11,385,000 shares, sales that generated over $200 million. At the time of the IPO, LifeTime had reported revenues of $74 million and liabilities of $309 million. As of the summer of 2010, LifeTime shares were selling for around $36 a share, representing a market value of over $1.5 billion. LifeTime's performance as a public company has generally been a bright spot for the industry.
- *Town Sports International (TSI), New York, New York*. TSI, which was founded in the early 1970s, grew to be one of the largest players in the industry over the last part of the 1990s and the beginning of the 2000s. This growth was the result of both acquisitions and organic growth fueled by debt, which, in many cases, was costly debt. In the summer of 2006, two years after LifeTime Fitness went public, TSI went public, offering 8.95 million shares at $12.90 a share (total offering of $125 million). At closing, TSI was selling for $13.25 and sold 8.9 million shares. The sale raised a considerable level of funds that were used to pay down the company's debt. As of the summer of 2010, TSI was trading at under $3 a share, which reflected a market value of $65.3 million.

The beginning of the new millennium marked the start of a new era for franchising in the fitness business.

❑ Franchise Clubs Take a Leading Role in Growing the Industry

The second major trend to emerge during the first decade of the 21st century was the rapid development of franchise operations, especially franchise operations dedicated to either 24-hour key card access, low cost, or both. While franchising in the fitness business has been around for decades, it was during the first decade of the 2000s that the practice took off. Prior to 2000, the most established franchise fitness operations were Powerhouse Gyms (over 300 franchise operations globally), which began in the 70s, Gold's Gym (over 600 franchise operations globally), which began franchising in the 1980s, Lady of America, which began franchising in the 80s and currently has over 175 franchise operations (making it the second largest women's-only franchise), World Gym (over 200 franchise operations globally), which began franchising in the 1980s, and Curves, which began franchising in the 1990s and is the world's largest fitness franchise.

The beginning of the new millennium marked the start of a new era for franchising in the fitness business. In large part, this sea-change was spurred on by Curves, which got its start in the 1990s. Subsequently, it became the largest fitness franchise in the world, with approximately 8,000 locations around the globe (at it's peak Curves had nearly 10,000 franchisees).

The question arises concerning why franchising blossomed during this particular time period. A number of reasons can be advanced regarding why franchising took hold at this particular point in time, including:

- The ability to establish niche franchise models that could serve new market segments (e.g., women, adults over 50, kids, express workouts, etc.), especially the huge demand for convenient and affordable fitness
- A growing market of young professionals who preferred to be their own bosses, rather than work for someone else
- The low cost of entry for entrepreneurs who wanted to start their own business (e.g., entry costs from as low as $30,000 to as high as $1.5 million, with an average of less than $250,000)
- The availability of low-cost capital, which made it relatively easy for entrepreneurs to finance their dreams
- The high margins and returns for franchisors (e.g., low overhead needed by most franchise organizations), which, in turn, attracted private equity to solid franchise models
- The packaged resources and marketing materials that francisors could make available to entrepreneurial start-ups

The current fitness franchise industry encompasses well over two dozen franchise models, including 21-Minute Convenience Fitness; Blitz Total Fitness (men's 20-minute express workouts); Club 50 Fitness Centers (adults over 50); Curves (women's express workouts); Fit After Fifty (adults over 50); Kid Fit (young children); Viva Fit (women's-only in Portugal); Mrs Sporty (women's-only express clubs in Germany); and Planet Fitness (Judgment Free Zone). The most successful of the franchise models, beyond Curves and Planet Fitness, have been two brands that emphasize 24/7 convenience at an affordable price—Anytime Fitness and Snap Fitness:

- *Anytime Fitness, Hastings, Minnesota.* The Anytime Fitness franchise founders, Chuck Runyon and Jeff Klinger, opened their first site in 2002. By 2010, their franchise operation had over 1300 open clubs. In 2008 alone, the company saw franchise clubs increase from 593 to 958, making it one of the top 15 fastest growing franchises in the world during that time period. The company model is based on offering a club that is available 24 hours, seven days a week, and which is affordable (less than $40 a month). The company provides its franchisee with a full turn-key package, including management software, insurance, security systems, initial and ongoing training for staff, programming elements, marketing support, and much more. The typical Anytime Fitness club ranges in size from 3,500 square feet to 5,000 square feet, with an average of 4,000 square feet. This relatively small footprint, along with the limited staff operating model

> The current fitness franchise industry encompasses well over two dozen franchise models.

An Anytime Fitness club

(Anytime clubs employ key-card access and are only staffed during limited hours), its low start-up cost (ranging from $44,000 to $300,000), and its low cost of operations make the franchises particularly attractive to potential suitors. Franchises pay an initial fee, ranging from $9,000 to $21,000, and a fixed monthly fee of $449. This combination of a solid business model, low start-up and operating costs, and relatively low franchise fees provides an appealing package for entrepreneurs.

- *Snap Fitness, Chahhassen, Minnesota.* The Snap Fitness franchise founder, Peter Tauton, founded the company in 2003 and opened his first club in 2004. By the end of 2004, the company had 18 franchises. Two years later, it had over 400 franchises. By 2010, Snap Fitness had over 1,000 open franchise operations. In 2009, Snap was rated best in category for franchises by *Entrepreneur Magazine*. Similar to Anytime Fitness, Snap offers its franchisees a total turn-key package that includes club models, management systems, site selection, marketing support, security systems, etc. Like Anytime Fitness, Snap Fitness centers offer affordable and convenient fitness to consumers, featuring facilities that are open 24/7, with full key-card access. According to the Snap franchise model, the cost of starting up, including all franchise fees, construction costs, and equipment expenditures, range from $77,000 to $250,000.

The noteworthy success of both the Anytime Fitness and Snap Fitness franchise models, like Curves before them, is based on their attractive brand proposition for consumers (24/7, small, and affordable), their low cost of entry and operations for entrepreneurs, excellent management and marketing support systems, and the organization's strong leadership.

❏ Sports Performance Centers for Youth

The ever-increasing obesity pandemic among the world's youth, as well as the growing field of organized youth sports, helped to spark a third facility trend of the decade—the development of youth sports performance centers. As America's youth continued to gain (often unwanted) weight, their parents worked longer hours, and organized youth sports grew in popularity, entrepreneurs saw a unique opportunity to bring a new business model to the industry. This new model, involving sports performance centers, experienced its beginnings at the start of the century and built momentum as the decade commenced. These centers focused on providing structured fitness programs that were targeted at improving the sports performance of youth, primarily those young athletes between the ages of 8 and 16, with those individuals between the ages of 13 and 16 comprising the largest audience. While the primary focus of these facilities was on improving the performance level of young athletes, the centers also showcased the value of their programs with regard to fighting the obesity and sedentary-living pandemic that is afflicting the children of the entitlement generation. The leading players in this market, all of which happen to be franchise operations (an attribute that also makes them a part of the evolving fitness franchise market), include Frappier Acceleration (now Athletic Republic), Velocity Sports, and Parissi Speed Schools.

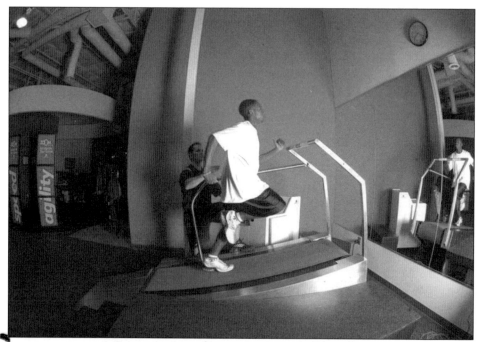

A Zoom sports performance center in Frisco, Texas

❏ The High-Volume, Low-Priced (HVLP) Clubs

Over the last few years, a new fitness club model has emerged, the "HVLP" club. The low-priced club model is based on offering consumers an exercise experience that features "minimalistic amenities and staffing." These low-priced clubs typically sell club memberships for under $20 U.S. a month, and in Europe for less than 20 euros a month. Ray Algar, a highly respected UK consultant (Oxygen Consulting), has identified five primary features that define a HVLP (referred to as a low-cost gym in Europe) club:

- 24-hour access (i.e., members can access the gym 24/7), at least on weekdays
- Gym only (i.e., the clubs only offer access to fitness equipment)
- Limited-to-no staffing (i.e., one staff person maximum or no staff on duty)
- Heavy technology (i.e., technology employed extensively to facilitate nearly all operating functions, such as membership sales, exercise prescription, exercise and nutritional guidance, information dissemination, etc.)
- Low price (i.e., 50 percent lower pricing than the industry average for the market)

While these five features are typically the defining attributes of HVLP clubs, several other common characteristics of these facilities also exist, such as no programming (e.g., no group classes, no personal training, etc.), no amenities (e.g., no towels, the showers involve usage fees, amenities are available through, no childcare, etc.), and total useable area of 15,000 to 25,000 square feet (averaging 1500 to 2500 meters).

The low-priced gym model requires an extremely high level of membership turnover, with facilities often allocating as little as one square foot per membership. For example, the typical McFit club in Germany has 7,000 to 8,000 members in a 2,500 meter facility, while a Planet Fitness club in the U.S. may have as many as 15,000 members in 20,000 square feet (more likely 5,000 to 6,000 members in 15,000 square feet). Some of the most recognizable "low-cost" club operators include:

- McFit, Germany (memberships at just under 17 Euros a month)
- Gym Group, UK (memberships at under 20 Euros a month)
- Planet Fitness, U.S. (memberships at $10 a month)
- Retro Fitness, U.S. (memberships at $19.95 a month)
- Fitness 19 (memberships at $10 a month)
- Fit N Fast, Australia (memberships as low as $7 a week)

Recently, several main-street club operators have introduced their own personal low-cost brands to the market, including:

- Equinox (under the brand name, Blink Fitness, with memberships between $15 and $20 a month)
- Crunch (franchise models, with dues ranging from $9.95 to $19.95 a month)

The low-priced club model is based on offering consumers an exercise experience that features "minimalistic amenities and staffing."

- Bally (dues program at $19.99 a month and expects to have close to 90 clubs offering such a membership package by the end of 2011)

Truth be known, the verdict remains out as to whether this recent expansion in the number of "low-cost" clubs will prove to be an industry innovation or a temporary trend in the health/fitness club facility industry.

❏ Non-Traditional Fitness Facilities

Beyond the club models already mentioned, the 21st century has seen non-profits and other less traditional fitness models emerge as key players in attracting today's consumers. These models include:
- Religious based fitness centers, such as the Young Men's Christian Association (now referred to as the Y) and Jewish Community Centers, which serve local communities
- Univesity-based fitness centers (serving faculty, students and the public)
- Military-based fitness centers (serving the military and their families)
- Park and Recreation fitness centers (serving residents in local municipalities)
- Apartment-based fitness centers (serving apartment residents)
- Hotel based fitness centers (serving both hotel guests and the public)
- Personal training studios
- Pilates and yoga studios
- Group-cycling studios

The verdict remains out as to whether this recent expansion in the number of "low-cost" clubs will prove to be an industry innovation or a temporary trend in the health/fitness club facility industry.

Legendary Individuals Who Influenced the Industry

Chapter 8

*"Myths and legends die hard…we love them
for the extra dimension they provide, the illusion
of near-infinite possibility to erase the narrow
confines of most men's reality."*
— Hunter Thompson

*"He who influences the thoughts of his time
influences the times that follow."*
— Elbert Hubbard

The Making of a Legend

Legends tend to be characterized by their ability to think outside the box and their ability to transform their perceptions of the "possible" into the authentic threshold of "reality." In other words, they have the ability and the courage to overcome the narrow confines of the thinking of others. In the process, they have the innate ability to affect the world in which they reside. The legendary people who have influenced the fitness industry are no exception. Their insights and efforts have impacted the industry in enumerable ways.

> Legends tend to be characterized by their ability to think outside the box and their ability to transform their perceptions of the "possible" into the authentic threshold of "reality."

This chapter, as well as the two chapters that follow, detail the legendary individuals whom the authors believe have had the greatest impact on shaping the fitness industry, as well as the equipment innovations and the outstanding clubs that have changed the landscape of the fitness industry forever. Somewhat similar to any attempt to develop an "all-anything" list, a certain degree of subjectivity is involved in the effort. This endeavor is no different. Of course, readers are invited to put together their own list.

This chapter begins by identifying legendary icons who had a discernible historical impact on the fitness industry. The chapter also includes a list of individuals, who, while not icons, had a consequential influence on the evolution of the fitness industry.

Fourteen Icons Who Changed the Industry

Charles Atlas (1892–1972)

Atlas, born Angelo Siciiano in New York, was a protégé of Bernarr Macfadden. In 1921 and again in 1922, Atlas entered Macfadden's "World's Most Perfectly Developed Man Competition." In both years, he won, in one instance beating over 775 competitors for the title. After his second victory, Mafadden, sensing a great talent, took Atlas under his tutelage. Macfadden then introduced Atlas to Dr. Frederick Tilney, a homeopathic physician and physical culturist. Together, Macfadden, TIlney, and Atlas wrote a training course on muscle control and isometric opposition exercises that encompassed 12 lessons initially, and a thirteenth lasting lesson. The course was promoted through Macfadden's magazines, and later in newspapers, magazines, books, and comic books. By 1929, the three men had incorporated as Charles Atlas, Ltd, a mail-order and in-home exercise company. Atlas became even more famous when he teamed with Charles Roman, a recent marketing and business graduate from New York University. Roman, who became the marketing genius behind Charles Atlas, Ltd. coined the phrase "dynamic tension," and created the themes for all of the Charles Atlas advertisements that promoted the course, including: "Hey Skinny,", "97-Pound Weakling," among others.

Concurrently, Roman began placing ads in comic books, which, at the time (the period of the Great Depression), were incredibly popular among young

Bill Pearl Enterprises
Charles Atlas

men. It was the unique blend of Atlas' persona and personal selling skills, Roman's incredible marketing savvy, and the arrival of the Great Depression that took Atlas to the pinnacle of the field of mail-order fitness courses (it should be noted that his courses are still selling, 80 years after they were introduced). What set Charles Atlas apart the most and helped establish a legacy that still stands today, both as a legend of physical culture and an icon in business, was his unique ability to personalize his program for everyone, while still maintaining a high-volume sales approach. Atlas wrote letters to all of his students, creating what he believed and his students felt, was an intimate bond between teacher and student. *Forbes Magazine* called Atlas a "super salesman," but his millions of students saw him as their teacher, coach, and personal guide to physical perfection.

Catherine Beecher (1800–1878)

Beecher, whose life mission was "to find happiness in living to do good," was renowned for her contributions to advancing the need for physical education, physical conditioning, and proper nutrition for women. Beecher co-founded her first school for women in 1823, called the Hartford Female Seminary in Hartford, Connecticut. It was during her tenure at the Hartford Seminary that she introduced calisthenics exercises for women. In 1831, she wrote an essay, entitled "A Course in Calisthenics for Young Ladies," which expounded on her approach to exercise for women. Later in 1833, after moving to Cincinnati, Ohio, where she and her father opened the Western Female Institute, she expanded upon her innovative callisthenic exercises for women involved performing light exercises for multiple repetitions, usually to music. Over the next several decades, her callisthenic exercises for women grew in prominence, finally gaining acceptance as proper for women of the period. In 1856, she authored a book, entitled *Physiology and Calisthenics for Schools and Families*, in which she laid out her style of gymnastics for women. Beecher's callisthenic exercises for women were ground-breaking and led to her being anointed in many circles as the founder of American-style gymnastics for women. Over the decades, she became the leading proponent of regular physical exercise and proper nutrition for women and their importance to the overall health and well-being of women. In 1873, she authored another book, entitled *Housekeeper and Health Keeper*," in which she laid out guidance for physical exercise and proper dieting for women. One year later, she had another book released, called *Educational Reminiscences and Suggestions*," in which she expounded further on the importance of regular physical activity for women.

Leo Durlacher (1844–1924)

The forefather of master trainers and strength coaches, as well as a physical culture legend, Durlacher was known to historians as Professor Attila. Professor Attila trained many of the great strength athletes of the late 19th and early 20th centuries. Born in 1844 in Germany, Durlacher established his first gym in Brussels, Belgium in the 1880's, opened a second gym in London in the late 1880s, and finally founded Professor Attila's Athletic Studio and School of Physical Culture in New York, New York in 1894. He was the creator of the Globe barbell, the Roman chair, and the Roman column. More than anything else, Professor Attila is known for the great athletes he trained, individuals such as Lionel Strongfort (a famous English strongman), George Rolandow (the first to lift the Rolandow Challange Barbell), Louis Cyr (a Canadian strongman and onetime world's strongest man), Warren Lincoln Travis (a famous American strongman), Gentleman Jim Corbett (onetime heavyweight boxing champion), and Eugen Sandow, possibly the most famous strongman of all-time. He also trained some of the top business professionals and dignitaries of the period, including Cornelius and Alfred Vanderbilt, J.P. Morgan, Jr, Baron Rothschild, John Philip Sousa, Alexander III, Czar of Russia, King Edward VII of England, King George of Greece and queen Mother Alexandra of England. Lastly, Professor Attila was one of the first proponents of progressive resistance training for women, and also of weight training to combat the effects of aging.

Professor Attila at age 50

Frederick Ludwig Jahn (1778–1852)

Frederick Ludwig Jahn is referred to as the father of modern gymnastics and the developer of Turn, a physical culture club built around gymnastics and the mutual social and patriotic interests of its members. Jahn was the creator of the pommel horse, parallel bars, horizontal bars, vaulting blocks, and the ladder, all of which have become mainstays in athletic facilities of the future. In 1811, Jahn established what is believed to be the first gymnastics club, Public Turn Platz, the Public Turn Platz was an open field that offered men and boys mass exercise classes that were designed to help them become physically fit to protect their country. Jahn's initial Turn not only incorporated exercises that employed parallel bars, the pommel horse, and horizontal bars, it also integrated dumbbells and Indian Clubs into structured classes. By 1860 over 150 Turns, often called Turnverein, had spread across the globe, offering mass exercise and gymnastics to men and boys. Without question, the evolution of German-style gymnastics owes much of its success to the efforts of Frederich Jahn.

Arthur Jones (1926–2007)

Jones is one of the true pioneers of the fitness industry. The inventor of the Nautilus Variable Resistance Machine, Jones changed an entire industry when he introduced his revolutionary type of training equipment to the industry. While Jones had been involved in fitness previously (having created a Nautilus prototype as early as the late 1940s), it was his development of the revolutionary Nautilus CAM and variable resistance that changed how people exercised and how clubs and gyms presented their product to the marketplace. His efforts fostered the development of the modern equipment company, when his Nautilus Company became the largest manufacturer of fitness equipment, achieving sales of close to $75 to $80 million (equivalent to $250 to $270 million in current dollars) at its pinnacle in the late 1970s. Jones' most consequential contribution to the world of fitness may not have been the Nautilus equipment he brought forth in 1970, but rather his core principles of training, including performing one set to exhaustion, super-slow controlled concentric and eccentric training, and approximately 20-minute circuits. Forty years after he introduced Nautilus to the world, the Nautilus name remains the "Kleenex" of the equipment industry, and his principles of training remain deeply ingrained in the lexicon of modern functional training.

> Jones changed an entire industry when he introduced his revolutionary type of training equipment to the industry.

Jack LaLanne (1914–2011)

LaLanne was possibly the most influential fitness legend of the post-World War II era. In 1951, he became the host of a nationally syndicated TV show—the *Jack LaLanne Show*, America's first telecast dedicated to the pursuit of fitness. LaLanne was a natural fit for this new medium. His combination of charisma, sense of humor, enthusiasm, knowledge, and of course physical appearance, made him a star. More significantly, LaLanne's show brought fitness into the homes of millions. Every morning across America, housewives took part in following the wholesome form of exercise that LaLanne preached. As a consequence, the gospel of living a fit lifestyle spread rapidly across America. Over the next 34 years, concluding in 1985, Jack LaLanne became the face of fitness. In addition to his fame as a TV personality, LaLanne's influence extended much further. He is credited with having invented the "Smith machine" (named after Rudy Smith, a club pioneer who brought the piece to market) and the leg extension machine, both staples of the modern fitness center. LaLanne was also the most recognized name in the health spa and gym business. For an extended period of time, his name was associated with over 200 clubs, initially when he lent his name to Ray Wilson's European Health Spas, which, in turn, became Jack LaLanne European Health Spas, and later with Bally, with whom he licensed his name. Until his passing in early 2011, LaLanne, even though he was in his nineties, was still one of the most sought-after speakers and personalities in the field of fitness.

Pehr Henrik Ling (1776–1839)

Ling is often referred to as the father of Swedish Medical Gymnastics (originally referred to as Swedish Pedagogic Gymnastics), a modality grounded in four core principles—medical, military, pedagogical, and aesthetics. Along with German-style gymnastics, Swedish-style gymnastics served as one of the two primary elements of training for all future forms of physical training introduced in Europe and the United States. Swedish Medical Gymnastics also become one of the building blocks for three therapeutic forms of medicine that came to prominence in the 20th Century (Ling's founding principles and techniques had a substantial impact on these newer forms of medical therapeutic treatment); chiropracty, osteopathy and Swedish massage.

Pehr Henrik Ling

Bernarr Macfadden (1868–1955)

Macfadden (his original name was Bernard McFadden), often called the father of physical culture and possibly the most influential fitness personality of the

Bernarr Macfadden

late 19th and early 20th centuries, first came to prominence in the 1890s, taking the world stage at about the same time as Eugen Sandow. Macfadden opened his first studio in 1887, marketing himself as a "kinestherapist" (the first person to coin this phrase) and a teacher of higher physical culture. In 1894, he created the Macfadden exerciser. By 1899, he had opened a series of physical culture clubs. In 1899, he published his first issue of *Physical Culture*, a magazine dedicated to the pursuit of physical culture and health, a publication that by 1903 had circulation of over 100,000. The magazine ran for 50 years, and had the longest circulation run of any health and fitness magazine in U.S. history. He also published *Beauty and Health for Women*. During the late 1800s, Macfadden toured the country, often with his family, promoting his brand of physical culture, while also serving as the first "global advocate" of physical culture, training, and healthy eating. Macfadden's influence endured well into the 20th century, with the publication of the first edition of *Macfadden's Encyclopedia of Physical Culture* in 1911, a publication that had seven separate editions. By the third edition, the encyclopedia, which began as one volume, had evolved into eight volumes, which covered topics ranging from anatomy and physiology to the diagnosis and treatment of disease. Macfadden also established the Macfadden Healthatorium, first in Battlecreek, Michigan and later in Chicago, Illinois. The Healthatorium was a school for educating aspiring physical culturists in alternative health practices. He also established the Bernarr Macfadden Institute, a school for training professionals in physcultopathy. In the early 1900s, Macfadden was involved in a short-lived experiment, called Physical Culture City, a town built in New Jersey that was dedicated to healthy living. Macfadden eventually became a multi-millionaire as the result of his magazine publication business, which expanded itself from publishing health and physical culture magazines to publishing a variety of magazines, such as *True Romance, True Detective, Dream World*, etc. One particular quote that appeared in a 1906 issue of his *Physical Culture Magazine* speaks to Macfadden's vision for the future of fitness, his passion, and contributions to spreading the gospel of fitness during the late 19th and early 20th centuries:

> *"When the importance of physical culture*
> *is recognized, when men and women realize its*
> *true importance, it will enter into every phase*
> *of human life. There is hardly a question in life*
> *which physical culture should not be a part."*

Johann GutsMuth (1759–1839)

GutsMuth is known as the grandfather of German-style physical education and the first individual to introduce an organized curriculum for gymnastics or calisthenics training. In 1793, GutsMuth, wrote a 700-page book on gymnastic exercises, entitled *Gymnastics for Youth: Or a Practical Guide to Healthful and Amusing Exercise; for the Use of Schools*. GutsMuth's publication featured exercises for young boys and girls. Over the years, GutsMuth's book became the "bible" of German-style gymnastics or physical training. GutsMuth is also credited with creating the "Weaver stick," a six-foot long wooden stick that was notched at intervals for adding weights. The Weaver stick was primarily used for training the forearms, as well as the entire upper body. Along with Swedish-style gymnastics, German-style gymnastics served as one of the two primary elements of training for all future forms of physical training.

Johann GutsMuth

Bill Pearl Enterprises

Augie Nieto (1960–present)

Nieto, possibly more than any modern-day fitness professional, helped to shape the way the fitness industry operates today. Nieto, one of the co-founders of Life Fitness, was initially the chief sales advocate for the Lifecyle, working as a salesman for Ray Wilson. While he was not the inventor of the Lifecycle, Nieto was very instrumental in making Lifecycle as successful as it subsequently became. By any objective measure, Lifecycle changed the way people exercised in clubs. By the late 1970s, the Lifecycle was the top selling piece of cardiovascular equipment in the industry, and would help foster the development of the largest equipment manufacturer in the world. While the introduction of the Lifecycle and the creation of Life Fitness will be Nieto's primary legacy, it is his other contributions to the industry that may actually last longer. Life Fitness, which he founded, took the lead in making cardiovascular fitness equipment a staple of clubs in the twentieth century. As the president of Life Fitness, his support and sponsorship of the fledgling club association, IHRSA, helped provide the financial impetus for the association's rapid ascension as a global industry trade association. Life Fitness also helped sponsor numerous educational events that were hosted by IHRSA, as well as a sponsor of several global events that introduced fitness around the globe. It was Nieto's vision and financial support that helped initiate the first European leaders meeting, as well as helped establish similar global events around the world. Nieto was a compelling apostle for fitness, using the platform of Life Fitness and subsequently his other ventures to continue to promote the benefits of fitness worldwide.

Eugen Sandow (1867–1925)

In the 1880s, Sandow, born in Prussia and a student of Professor Attila, established himself on the world stage. Over a period of 30 years, beginning in the 1880s, Sandow established himself as one of the most well-known strongmen in the history of physical culture. Sandow was a strongman, entertainer, health educator, trainer, and celebrity. He established numerous records in strongman competitions, having defeated the likes of Apollo, Cyclops, Sampson, and other strongmen of that era. He is considered to be the first bodybuilder. His interest in bodybuilding is reflected by his efforts to actually measure the dimensions of Greek statues to identify the ideal proportions for the male physique. His feats of strength are still among the greatest of all-time, which is particularly noteworthy for a man that weighed less than 200 pounds. He developed the "Sandow physical training leg machine," as well as special-grip dumbbells. He also authored numerous books, including *Sandow's System of Physical Training* (1894); *Strength and How to Obtain It* (1897); *The Gospel of Strength According to Sandow* (1902); and *Bodybuilding by Sandow* (1904). In addition, he wrote numerous articles for magazines, including an article that appeared in an 1894 issue of *Cosmopolitan*, entitled "How to Preserve Health and Attain Strength." He also had his own magazine, *Sandow's Magazine*, that was published in 1905. In 1897, he opened a gym facility, The Institute of Physical Culture, that was dedicated to providing advanced techniques of training to up-and-coming professionals in the field of physical culture.

Dudley Allen Sargent, M.D. (1849–1924)

Sargent might be considered the "father" of evidence-based physical education, as well as the principal advocate of variable resistance training machines. Sergeant's career as a physical educator and fitness icon began in his youth, when he got involved in gymnastics. Subsequently, he went on to become a professional circus gymnast. By the age of 19, he was a medical student at Yale, where his interests evolved to focus on the scientific basis of physical education. In 1879, he was appointed as an assistant professor of physical education at Harvard and the director of the Hemenway Gymnasium, also at Harvard. At approximately the same time that he was appointed to the Harvard faculty, he established a private gym in Cambridge, Massachusetts, called the Sanatory Gymnasium, which catered to women at the Harvard Annex (an establishment that later became Radcliffe).

During his tenure at Harvard, he went on to pursue his two visions. The first was to study, research, and codify the perfect physical proportions of the human body, which lead him to undertake approximately 10,000 physical assessments. His pursuit of codifying anthropometric measurements and using the collected data to develop personalized exercise programs for each individual has led many to refer to him as the "grandfather of fitness testing." Sargent's second vision was to create machines that would bring balance to the development of the human physique. Ultimately, these two visions drove

> Sargent might be considered the "father" of evidence-based physical education.

him to establish an entire system based on the use of physical measurements and machines that would allow any man or women to achieve the "universal perfect muscular form."

Sargent designed his own exercise equipment, occasionally in collobaration with the famous Swedish physical culturist and physician, Gustav Zander. During his tenure at Harvard, he developed approximately 36 distinct variable resistance machines, including the chest pulley, and the abdominal pulley, as well as numerous other machines. He is also credited with developing the pulley systems (adjustable weight plates on pulleys) that became a staple of neary every gym in America during the early 1900's, and the forfather of today's variable resistance machines. One interesting creation of Sargent's was the counter-weighted parallel bar, which allowed weaker individuals to perform dips (an early version of the StairMaster Gravitron). Finally, many of the exercises he designed for his pulley machines, such as the wood chop, sawing, and swimming, are staples of today's functional training protocols.

Dudley Allen Sargent

Bill Pearl Enterprises

Vic Tanny

Vic Tanny (1912–1985)

Tanny might well be considered the father of modern health clubs. In 1947, he opened a new type of gym in Los Angeles, a facility dedicated to serving the new middle-class suburban market. His new clubs, aptly named Vic Tanny's, welcomed both men and women. His clubs, different than most other facilities, focused on creating a welcoming environment for the average American by featuring mirrors, carpet, chrome, saunas, pools, and gym areas. Tanny created the first "modern health club." His clubs sold memberships on contract, with consumers having the opportunity to purchase a six-month contract, or if they prefered, a permanent seven-year contract. By 1960, Vic Tanny's had evolved from a single club to 84 facilities with approximately one million members and $24 million in annual sales ($176 million in current dollars). As such, Vic Tanny's became the largest club operator in the U.S. and the first large-scale chain of clubs in America. Vic Tanny's holds claim to more than being just the first modern health club or the first major chain of health clubs. Tanny's clubs were also the genesis of the hard-sale, price-discounting, and high-volume, do-anything-to-get-the-customer-to-join approach to membership sales. In an article that appeared in *Time Magazine* in 1961, Tanny is quoted as saying, *"volume is what counts."* While the Vic Tanny organization had its problems (e.g., sales tactics, deceitful selling practices, etc.), it was Tanny's innovative approach to club positioning, his introduction of membership contracts, and the fact that he was able to create the first club dynasty that remains his primary legacy to the fitness industry.

Ray Wilson (1928–present)

Wilson, an entrepreneur of incredible talent, was one of the pioneers of the modern fitness club industry. Starting in 1952 and continuing until as late as 2005 Wilson created more than 10 distinct chains of clubs, some of whose legacy continues until today. During the 1950s, Wilson founded four club chains. During the early 60s, he developed another four club chains. Among the groups he founded were American Health Studios, Silhouette Figure Salons, Silhouette International, Club International, President's Health Clubs, and European Health Spas. In the 1970s, he founded Family Fitness Centers, which grew to 72 clubs in California and were eventually sold to 24 Hour Fitness. Wilson's clubs introduced the alternate-day concept for health clubs, wherein men used the clubs three days a week (usually Tuesday, Thursday, and Saturday), women used the club three days a week (typically Monday, Wednesday, and Friday), and on Sundays, the day was split. He introduced both spa pools (involving a whirlpool, an apparatus for which he takes credit for launching in club facilities) and recreational pools to the club mix. During the 1970s, Wilson also purchased the rights to Lifecycle from its creator, Dr. Keene Dimmick. Together with a young Augie Nieto, the two industry icons sold the Lifecycle to the fitness industry. During the early part of the 21st century, he partnered in opening the California Fitness chain, which was the first "Western-style" gym to open in Hong Kong, a chain that later expanded to other regions of Asia (the chain was subsequently sold to 24 Hour Fitness).

Ray Wilson

Fourteen Remarkable Individuals Who Impacted the Industry

Kenneth Cooper, MD (1931–present)

Cooper pioneered the term "aerobics," and with it, established a new field of study and practice. Dr. Cooper coined the word "aerobics," as a by-product of his efforts with his first book, *Aerobics*, which was published in 1968. Cooper began his lifelong involvement in fitness as a member of the military as a flight surgeon and as the director of the Aerospace Medical Laboratory. During his tenure in these roles with the military, he developed the 12-minute fitness test and the 1.5-mile fitness test for cardiovascular capacity, both of which remain benchmark field tests of cardiovascular capacity and aerobic fitness. He is the originator of "aerobic points," a quantitative measure of the relative amount of cardiovascular work performed, based on the mode, intensity, and duration of the activity. Aerobic points became an industry standard for measuring aerobic activity. As the result of his work in the area of aerobics, Cooper helped establish an entire genre of exercise and exercise equipment. Over the last 40 years, Cooper has continually advanced the field of fitness through research conducted at his research facilities in Dallas. Much of his research, which was conducted at his own facility, supported what appeared in the Surgeon General's Report on Physical Activity and Health, which was released in 1996. Currently, in his late 70s, Dr. Cooper remains one of the most sought-after speakers in the area of physical activity and health.

Thomas K. Cureton, Jr. (1901–1992)

During the last half century of his lifetime, Cureton was the recognized leader and steward of America's fitness movement. Actively engaged in teaching, research, publishing, speaking, and working with a variety of professional associations in the field, Cureton had a deep and lasting impact on how exercise is conducted and perceived around the world. Unlike most of the individuals who preached the "gospel" of exercise and health during the 20th century, Cureton was the only fitness enthusiast who produced the research to substantiate his attitudes and beliefs regarding the positive influence of physical activity on health. His extensive efforts in this regard continue to influence the critical role that fitness and exercise play in the acquisition and maintenance of good health.

> T. K. Cureton had a deep and lasting impact on how exercise is conducted and perceived around the world.

Edmond Desbonnet (1868–1953)

Edmond Desbonnet is recognized by iron-game (e.g., bodybuilding and weightlifting) historians as the "Founder of Physique Culture in Europe." He believed strongly in the connection of a healthy body to a healthy mind. He opened one of the great schools (e.g., gyms) of physical culture (e.g., The School of Physical Culture) in Lille, France in 1885. The gym had an indoor track, martial arts training areas, gymnastic apparatus, and large quantities of resistance training equipment. He pioneered the use of large mirrors in the gym setting which allowed students and members to objectively assess their progress. In addition, his gym was possibly the first gym to use personal testimonies accompanied by stereographic photographs as part of its marketing effort. During its prime, his club was home to the finest strongmen and physical culture enthusiasts from around the globe, having mentored or influenced some of the most influential strongmen of the late 1800s and early 1900s. He was the author of at least six books on physical culture that promoted his approach to progressive resistance training. He is the founder of *La Culture Physique Magazine*, which was first published in 1904 and remained in circulation until 1971. Lastly, he organized the first international physique contest that was held in Europe. On a more personal level, he was awarded the prestigious Attila Trophy for his all-round athletic ability in 1894.

Dale Dibble (1920–2010)

Dibble pioneered the multisport club model, when he added fitness to the offering of his original indoor tennis club, Cederdale, which opened in 1971. Seeing beyond fitness or tennis, he visualized his club as a family-oriented, one-stop shop for everything recreational. What started out as a four court indoor tennis club with 200 members evolved into a 175,000-square foot sport resort,

Dale Dibble

serving approximately 8,500 members. His innovations included the addition of outdoor ball fields (e.g., baseball and softball), and minature golf courses, the creation of clubs within a club, and the development of corporate outings. Dibble also brought forth one of the first club management software systems. Dibble was one of the founding fathers of IRSA (later changed to IHRSA). In 2001, IHRSA renamed its distinguished service award as the Dale Dibble Distinguished Service Award.

Bob Hoffman (1898–1985)

Known as the "father of American weightlifting," Hoffman influenced physical culture, particularly weightlifting, for a period of approximately 40 years. Hoffman initially got involved in the business of fitness equipment in 1929, when he acquired a building on North Broad Street in York Pennsylvania with a partner, where he began to manufacturer oil burners and barbells. Around the same time, he created a weightlifting club, called the York Oil Burner Athletic Club, that soon became home to some of America's greatest weightlifters. In 1932, he incorporated his Athletic Club into the building that housed his oil burner and barbell manufacturing business. During that same year, after forming a business relationship with one of his mentors, George Jowett, he created the Strength and Health Publishing Company. The new company, with Jowett as editor, subsequently published the first issue of *Strength and Health Magazine* in 1932 (the magazine was a twist on the older British magazine, *Health and Strength*). Hoffman's magazine initially promoted physical culture, based on the principles of Jowett and Hoffman's past efforts with *Strength* magazine. Soon after, the magazine became the vehicle that allowed Hoffman to actively promote and peddle his products and perspectives to physical culture enthusiasts and aspiring young men around the country. In the early 30s, Hoffman purchased the vestiges of Earle Liederman's once enormously successful mail-order business. Shortly after that, in 1935, Hoffman purchased the assets of the Milo Barbell Company, once the leading manufacturer of weightlifting equipment in the United States. By 1938, Hoffman had not only founded the York Barbell Company, he was also firmly established as the "guru" of physical culture and weightlifting in America. By 1938, he had taken a dominant, nearly monopolistic hold on the physical culture business in America. With a firm grasp on the manufacturing side of weightlifting, a publishing company that had the top physical culture magazine of the time, and a club training America's leading weightlifters and bodybuilders, Hoffman was on his way to dominating the industry, and, in effect, reshaping the landscape of physical culture in America. Hoffman would later go on to publish several books on weight training that emphasized his approach to training, as well as promoted his products. Over the course of four decades, his empire became the most influential force in physical culture, with his equipment appearing in homes and gyms across America and his weightlifting methods adhered to by hosts of young men, and even women, across the U.S.

Bob Hoffman

Archibald MacLaren (1820–1884)

MacLaren was a visionary in physical conditioning and fitness and the most influential figure in the development of physical education programming in the U.K. His approach to physical conditioning was grounded in the latest information on anatomy, medicine, biomechanics, and physiology. As a result of his scientific approach to exercise, MacLaren clearly understood the importance of physical conditioning to the health of the average British citizen.

> MacLaren was a visionary in physical conditioning and fitness and the most influential figure in the development of physical education programming in the U.K.

In 1859, Archibald MacLaren established what is considered the first well-equipped gymnasium in England, at the University of Oxford. He was the first fitness professional to introduce the use of photographs and written records to document the success of his students. MacLaren also introduced the concepts of progressive resistance training and individualization to exercise programming, currently two of the mainstays in evidence-based exercise prescription according to the American College of Sports Medicine. He also was the first individual to advocate structured and individualized exercise programming for children, based on his observation that typical sports activities of the time did not promote overall health for the youth of the country. He is the founding member of the National Society of Physical Education in England and the former president of the National Physical Recreation Society of England. He is also well known for his book, entitled A System of Physical Education, a text that was first published in 1869.

Mark Mastrov (1964–present)

Mastrov founded and led 24 Hour Fitness from its inception in 1983, as a single Nautilus club, until 2005, when he and his equity partners sold the company to Forstmann Little & Company for $1.6 billion. Mastrov's influence on the industry is somewhat different than the other individuals listed in this chapter. Mastrov was not a physical culture guru or equipment innovator, instead he was a business entrepreneur, who had a clear vision, excellent understanding of the cultural landscape, a wonderful feel for marketing and promotion, a grasp of what consumers wanted from clubs, and a commitment to seeing his vision realized. Mastrov pioneered the concept of the 24/7 club, and was a leader in the endeavor to employ celebrity endorsements in the club business, an effort that included establishing several celebrity-branded facilities (e.g., Magic Johnson, Andre Agassi, Jackie Chan, Lance Armstrong, Derek Jeter, Yao Ming, etc.). Mastrov was also a pioneer in integrating the fitness club industry with the private equity arena. He was one of the first individuals to significantly leverage the relationship between private equity and the club business, when he partnered with McCown deLeeuw & Company. He was also a leader in developing a standardized club model that could be easily duplicated through organic development. Subsequently, working with his private equity partners, he also became a leader in rebranding acquisition clubs to fit the 24 Hour Fitness model. By the time he sold his business in 2005, it was the largest club company in the history of the industry, with over 400 clubs in multiple countries. It also had achieved the highest market valuation of any company in the industry. What many individuals aren't aware of is Mastrov's influence on the club industry in international markets, where both of his companies (e.g., formerly 24 Hour Fitness and currently his new private equity business, New Evolution Ventures) have invested in numerous successful club business ventures throughout Asia, Europe, and the Americas. His investments have included California Fitness, Asia; Planeta Fitness, Russia; Hard Candy Fitness Centers, Global; Ultimate Fighting Center Gyms, U.S.; Steve Nash Sports Clubs, Canada; and Energie in South America. As of 2010, he continues to invest in emerging markets (e.g., Asia, Latin America), emerging fitness club business models (e.g., UFC Gyms and Hard Candy Gyms), and the repositioning of formerly successful club brands (e.g., Crunch).

Missett is often referred to as the founder of group exercise.

John McCarthy (1937–present)

McCarthy was the first executive director of IRSA, which later was renamed IHRSA, serving in that position for the first 25 years of the Association's existence. McCarthy, working with the original founding members of IRSA, helped to build a global trade association that currently represents nearly 10,000 club owners around the world. When the association first started, McCarthy focused on building an organization that would support the core mission of promoting an association of quality clubs. Over the years, McCarthy, more than anyone in the industry, had an insightful vision of what the future held for the fitness industry. In the process, he led IRSA (and IHRSA) toward a global, all-encompassing effort to be the voice of the industry, both domestically in the U.S. and worldwide. He pioneered efforts to establish credibility for the industry, and led the way in helping club operators focus on developing their professionalism. His dynamic personality and incredible relationships skills enabled him to foster global relationships, which brought club operators from around the world together, thereby creating an Association that inspired innovation and sharing among its members. McCarthy also helped bring operators and vendors together. It was part of McCarthy's core vision that the health/fitness club industry would become an integral part of the American lifestyle, rather than just a discretionary luxury for individuals who could afford it. Without question, the fitness industry owes a huge debt of gratitude to his visionary leadership, when he served as the spokesperson for an industry starved to receive the attention it desperately needed and so well deserved.

Judi Sheppard Missett (1944–present)

Missett, a legend in the group-exercise and fitness industry, is often referred to as the founder of and the primary spokesperson for organized group exercise. Missett started her career as a dancer, joining a touring company at the age of 14. In 1969, while a student at Northwestern University in Chicago, Missett taught dance classes at a jazz studio. In the course of her teaching efforts, she discovered that most of her students were dancing, not to become professionals, but instead to lose weight, get in shape, and have fun. This

Jazzercise, Inc.

Judi Sheppard Missett

discovery led her to change the primary focus of her classes to "Just for Fun Dance," in which she created integrated dance movements, with movements from other activities, such as yoga, Pilates, resistance training, etc., to which she added music. Eventually, her classes became Jazzercise. Missett was the first popular fitness professional to use the VCR and videotapes to train instructors in her methods. The Jazzercise system also featured new routines (approximately 28) and music that were changed every 10 weeks, a process that kept classes interesting and motivational for students. Jazzercise has remained at the forefront of group fitness for over 40 years by constantly adapting to changing trends and by keeping the program true to Missett's original mission of making exercise fun and effective for people of all ages and fitness levels. Jazzercise is currently taught at approximately 3,200 locations, with as many as 20,000 classes taught weekly. Jazzercise is the originator and still the king of packaged group exercise programs. Jazzercise pioneered a field that has brought fitness to millions, and subsequently set the stage for entrepreneurs, such as Philip Mills and Les Mills international.

Michael O'Shea (1946–present)

Internationally recognized as a pioneer in the field of one-to-one fitness training, O'Shea founded the renowned Sports Training Institute in 1975 in New York

City, which subsequently grew to 10 locations, serving six states under his leadership. O'Shea's clubs were the first such facilities to require client's to receive medical clearance prior to participating in a fitness program. The Sports Training Institute was also a pioneer in developing personal training as a core part of its business. Currently, O'Shea serves as a contributing editor on health and exercise to *Parade Magazine*, a role he has held since 1985. He also is extensively involved in a number of philanthropic endeavors, including serving on the board of directors for the national USO organization, as well as helping to establish the exercise program at the Lighthouse for the Blind in Manhattan.

Bill Pearl (1930–present)

One of the most respected individuals in the health and fitness industry, Pearl has had an extensive and successful career as a bodybuilder, trainer, author, and exercise advocate. As a bodybuilder, Pearl won 10 major titles over a period of 22 years, including unprecedented (at the time) Mr. Universe honors four times. In 1978, he was inducted into the Hall of Fame of the World Body Building Guild. As a trainer, Pearl has coached more major bodybuilding contest winners than any other person in history. Operating gym facilities for more than three decades, he has helped develop 10 Mr. Universe and eight Mr. America winners. Pearl has also written several best-selling books, including *Getting Stronger*, *Keys to the INNER Universe*, and *Legends of the Iron Game*. As an articulate proponent of the benefits of exercise, Pearl is a much sought-after speaker who addresses groups around the world. He regularly appears at fitness-related events and conventions.

Bill Pearl

Joseph Pilates (1993–1967)

One of the pioneers in the fitness industry, Pilates developed the floor exercises that bear his name that are so widely popular in health/fitness clubs around the world. Not only did he create the Pilates method of exercise, he also invented the Pilates exercise equipment, as an outgrowth of his efforts (as a German national) working with individuals in an internment camp in England during WWI. His innovative equipment utilized the few items that were available to him as an internee, (for example, bed springs and beer key rings). The resultant resistant training apparatus was the forerunner of the Pilates equipment, such as the reformer and magic circle, that is currently employed in many gyms. The Pilates' exercise system was inspired by his attraction to Zen Buddhism and various Eastern practices as well as by the ancient Greek ideal of the perfection of man being grounded in the development of body, mind, and spirit.

Jackie Sorenson is credited with being the modern-day founder of "aerobic dancing", when she combined choreographed dance movements with "aerobic"-driven intensity.

Jackie Sorenson (1950–present)

Jackie Sorenson is credited with being the modern-day founder of "aerobic dancing", when she combined choreographed dance movements with "aerobic"-driven intensity. Her introduction to fitness started when she was asked by the Air Force to develop a television-oriented physical activity program for the wives of Air Force staff. From this introduction, Jackie brought her choreographed group exercise program to the YMCA of America, where it quickly spread to YMCAs throughout the U.S. By 1980, her aerobic dancing program was one of the most popular forms of exercise for women across the globe. Jackie also introduced two other innovative group exercise programs to the industry—Workout, which was a less intensely choreographed aerobic program, and Strong Step™, which utilized a step to increase lower body resistance.

Jackie has authored two books on fitness—*Aerobic Dancing* and *Jackie Sorenson's Aerobic Lifestyle Book*. She is an active member of the President's Council on Physical Fitness and Sport, and has been recognized for her contributions to the fitness industry by receiving IDEA's Lifetime Achievement Award and being inducted into *Club Industry Magazine's* Hall of Fame.

Harold Zinkin, Sr. (1922–2004)

Zinkin is one of the pioneers in the history of the fitness industry. A regular at "Muscle Beach" in the 1930s, Zinkin was an integral part of the group that started the then often-discussed physical fitness movement. In 1941, he won the first Mr. California bodybuilding title. Twelve years later, Zinkin moved to Fresno, California, where he started a chain of fitness centers. During this period, he designed the world's first pin-loaded weight training machine, which he patented in 1961. This piece of equipment became the renowned Universal Gym machine, which quickly became one of the most popular exercise machines in the world.

Innovative Equipment That Shaped the Industry

"No man ever made a great discovery without the exercise of imagination."
— George Henry Lewis

Ten Equipment Innovations
That Shaped the Industry

Dumbbell (5th Century B.C.)

The dumbbell, more than any other piece of resistance training equipment, changed the way people employed resistance work to train their bodies. The first dumbbells, called alteres or halteres, were created by the Greeks in the 5th century B.C. These early Greek dumbbells were made of wax, with shaved iron filings used to add weight. Ten centuries later, these exercise tools were called plummets. Subsequently, by the early 18th century, they had been renamed as dumbbells. The earliest 18th century dumbbells were constructed of wood, often with an iron filling to add weight. In the early era of the fitness industry, dumbbells became one of the "four horsemen" of fitness, along with the medicine ball, the Indian club, and the barbell.

> The dumbbell, more than any other piece of resistance training equipment, changed the way people employed resistance work to train their bodies.

Curtis Rowing Machine (1871)

The Curtis rowing machine, developed in 1871 by William B. Curtis, was the first piece of cardiovascular equipment designed solely for indoor training purposes. Curtis was an avid rower. As one of the founding members of the New York Athletic Club, which opened in 1868, he developed a piece of equipment that would allow individuals to train year-round, a rowing machine that involved the use of a flywheel and ratchet system. The Curtis rowing machine subsequently became a template for future rowing machines, which during the early 20th century, were the leading cardiovascular device in athletic clubs and gyms.

The Plate-Loaded Barbell (1902)

In 1902, Alan Calvert established the Milo Barbell Company, the first company to mass-produce barbells, dumbbells, globe bells, and kettlebells. While barbells and dumbbells had existed prior to the establishment of Calvert's company, Milo was the first to mass-produce barbells and dumbbells for both commercial and home use. Even more significant was the company's development of the plate-loaded barbell, which enabled users to easily adjust the amount of weight lifted. Prior to the plate-loaded barbell, most barbells and dumbbells featured a globe design that required the users to fill the globe with either sand, shot, or similar substance.

Quinton Treadmill (1952)

In 1952, Robert Bruce and Wayne Quinton developed the first commercial medical treadmill that was designed for use with human subjects (it should be noted that the first treadmill, the Level Power Treadmill, was actually developed over 75 years earlier, but was not designed for use by humans). Quinton and Dr. Bruce, who taught at the University of Washington, developed the treadmill

*The Quinton treadmill was the first
commercial treadmill that was designed
for use with human subjects.*

for testing the cardiovascular function of individuals. The Quinton treadmill, which was extremely well-built, substantially became a staple of medical centers and universities. The Quinton treadmill became the benchmark for the development of treadmills in the future, and even today, the original Quinton treadmills may have been the sturdiest ever made.

Universal Gym (1957)

In 1957, Harold Zinkin, a former Mr. California, invented the Universal multi-station machine. Zinkin's innovation was the first multi-station, selectorized resistance equipment manufactured and sold in the world. Zinkin patented his equipment, and shortly thereafter, introduced the first circuit programs that utilized his machine. By 1960, he had introduced the Mack series of multi-station machines, selling one unit per month. By 1964, Universal was selling one unit per week. Zinkin sold the company in 1968. The new owners continued to expand the Universal brand, introducing several series of exercise machines over the decades to come. The term "dynamic variable resistance," a designation for the mode of resistance provided by their machines, was patented by Universal in 1974. Over the years, Universal became the benchmark by which other companies developed their selectorized single and multi-station resistance training machines.

Lifecycle (1968)

The Lifecycle was invented in 1968 by Keene Dimmick. A few years later, Ray Wilson was introduced to the machine and quickly realized that it offered an entirely new dimension to the equipment that was currently in vogue in the club industry. Wilson subsequently purchased the rights to Lifecycle, and shortly thereafter, hired Augie Nieto, a college student (who would subsequently become one of the co-founders of Life Fitness), to bring the Lifecycle to market. Under the entrepreneurial spirit of Wilson and Nieto, the Lifecycle rapidly evolved into a positive symbol of the fitness industry. The Lifecyle offered both fitness consumers and health/fitness club operators a new and innovative approach to aerobic training. The Lifecycle 2000 was the first piece of aerobic training equipment to feature a standardized program for aerobic training—the "12-minute program."

Nautilus Variable Resistance Machines (1970)

One of the most ground-breaking fitness equipment innovations of any period in the history of the fitness industry was the Nautilus variable resistance machines, introduced in 1970 by Arthur Jones, the founder of Nautilus. The primary point of differentiation in the new Nautilus equipment was the Nautilus cam, a specially designed pulley mechanism that was shaped like a nautilus shell (hence the name Nautilus). When a cable with weights was pulled over the cam, the resistance experienced by the user varied, simulating, according to Arthur Jones, the natural strength curve of a muscle group going through its range of motion. The term "variable resistance" was subsequently coined by Nautilus to explain the adjustment in resistance that exercisers experienced while using the machines. In addition to the creation of the cam, Jones' efforts to develop individual training machines for each of the various main body parts also had a significant impact on the industry. These individualized pieces of equipment enabled gyms and clubs to design and incorporate full resistance training circuits.

The Nautilus Pullover machine

StairMaster 5000

StairMaster 5000 and StairMaster 4000 PT (1983)

The StairMaster 5000 was designed by Lanny Potts, one of the three co-founders of StairMaster Exercise Systems (founded in 1983). The first StairMaster 5000 (featuring rotating stairs) was introduced in 1984. Shortly after being brought to market, Nicholas Orlando and Randy Peterson, previously involved in the distribution of Nautilus products in the Northeast region, approached Potts about becoming exclusive distributors of the product. The two eventually purchased a substantial interest in the company and created Randall Sports/ Medical Products, which became the exclusive distributor of the StairMaster 5000. Two years later, in 1986, Randall Sports/Medical introduced the StairMaster 4000 PT mechanical stairstepper. The 4000 PT went on to become the single most popular piece of cardiovascular equipment in the 80s and early 90s. These two machines, initially the StairMaster 5000, and subsequently the StairMaster 4000 PT, revolutionized the cardiovascular equipment industry, which had previously relied mostly on upright bicycles and treadmills.

Cardio Theater (1989)

In 1991, Tony DeLeede, owner of Australian Bodyworks in Atlanta, Georgia, introduced Cardio Theater to the health/fitness club industry. DeLeede was the first individual in the health/fitness club field to identify the power of entertainment, when he discovered the Cardio Theater system which was created in 1989 by David Tate. DeLeede's vision of entertainment in the industry, combined with his incredible marketing savvy brought about a revolutionary change in the industry. Cardio Theater brought entertainment to the health/fitness club industry by providing facility members with a means to watch television, while they were exercising on equipment, particularly on cardiovascular equipment. The first Cardio Theater system involved televisions that were mounted on walls or ceilings, with special transmitters and receivers that permitted exercisers to connect a special headphone into a receiving unit that was attached to the cardiovascular equipment. Users selected one of several stations, and then watched their selection on a TV, while listening

Cardio Theater in the 90s

to it through their headset. The first Cardio Theater units employed hardwire technology and had a relatively small range of station options. Subsequently, however, the company switched to wireless transmitters and offered a broad array of viewing options. Cardio Theater pioneered the entertainment segment of the fitness equipment industry. Its efforts led to future entertainment-related offerings, such as Broadcast Vision, E-Zone, and later to integrated systems that featured imbedded screens, iPod connections, and satellite connections.

Precor EFX 544 (1995)

In 1995, Precor introduced the world to elliptical training when it introduced the EFX 544 Elliptical Trainer. With it, Precor revolutionized indoor cardiovascular training. Up until 1995, the most popular aerobic training equipment were Lifecycles, mechanical stairclimbers (pioneered by StairMaster), and treadmills. The EFX, as it became more commonly known in the industry, established an entirely new mode of training. The EFX was designed to provide users with a minimally impactful form of aerobic training that essentially eliminated the impact (i.e., load forces) of exercising on a treadmill, and featured an exercise experience that most users perceived as less intense and less discomforting than offered by most other forms of aerobic exercise. The EFX was the perfect fit for the members of baby boomer generation, who were reaching 40, and were looking for exercise that placed less stress on their joints. The EFX also found an audience among women, because of the machine's ability to work the gluteus region.

Six Remarkable Equipment Innovations That Impacted the Industry

Medicine Ball (3000 BC)

The medicine ball was developed around 3000 BC by the Greeks. Initially, medicine balls were made of animal skins and filled with sand. Primarily they were used to develop muscular strength and endurance. By the middle of the 18th century, the medicine ball had become one of the "four horsemen" of training, along with the dumbbell, the Indian club, and the barbell.

Indian Clubs (introduced to the West in 1832)

Indian clubs were developed by Indian physical culture enthusiasts who used the tools to prepare for serving in the military and participating in Indian-style wrestling. While no specific date can be attributed to their creation, it is known that Indian clubs were formally introduced to England in 1832 by Donald Walker and in 1866 to the U.S. by Sim Kehoe. Once physical culture specialists became aware of this exercise device, the Indian club became a staple of the training kits of physical culture enthusiasts.

Cable Pulley Systems (1880s)

The exact date when cable pulleys were introduced remains unknown. Many individuals attribute the development of cable pulley systems to Dudley Allen Sargent, director of the Hemenway Gymnasium at Harvard in the late 1890s and early 1900s. Sargent believed that in order to obtain a symmetrical physique, as well as balanced physical development, people needed to train with machines. As a result of his focus on machine-based training, he proceeded to develop a variety of pulley systems, which went on to become an integral training apparatus for aspiring and professional physical culturists, as well as average citizens attempting to improve their level of physical conditioning. The selectorized machines that currently exist in the industry owe their start to Sargent's early pulley systems.

Exercycle (1932)

In 1932, Gordon Berg invented the Exercycle. Berg was looking for a piece of equipment to use in combating a neuromuscular disorder that his wife inherited. In the process, he created the Exercycle, an exercise device that combined lower- and upper-body movements in a way that simulated rowing, swimming, cycling, and chin-ups. The bike was powered by a small motor that enabled users to go through a range of motion, with varying levels of resistance. After developing the machine, Berg established the Exercycle Corporation, which built and distributed the equipment. The Exercycle was the first piece of exercise equipment that focused on providing cross-functional conditioning, for both the neuromuscular and the cardiovascular systems.

*The StairMaster
Gravitron machine*

StairMaster Gravitron (1988)

In 1988, Randall Sports/Medical Products introduced another innovative product to the market, called the Gravitron. This machine was a pneumatic piece of resistance equipment that provided assistance to exercisers when they were performing dips, chin-ups, and pull-ups. The Gravitron enabled individuals, who previously had never been able to perform these exercises, to safely and effectively do these movements. Not only did the Gravitron allow users to perform these movements, no matter their age or fitness level, it added an element of "technology" that helped motivate many exercisers. The Gravitron became the template for future "assisted dip-chin machines" that quickly saturated the market in response to the Gravitron's incredibly successful introduction.

Ground Zero Cable Cross and Functional Training Circuit (1999)

In 1999, a newly formed company called Ground Zero, introduced the Ground Zero functional training line of resistance equipment. Designed by Roy Simonson, formerly the chief equipment designer for Cybex Eagle, the Ground Zero machine, particularly its Cable Cross, reintroduced functional movement training with resistance equipment to the fitness industry, especially personal trainers. The Ground Zero subsequently revolutionized the fitness equipment industry, as nearly all manufacturers sought to duplicate the success of this new type of resistance training circuit.

Innovative Companies and Facilities That Impacted the Industry

Chapter 10

*"Businesses planned for service are apt to succeed;
businesses planned for profit are apt to fail."*
— Nicholas Murray Butler

Fourteen Innovative Health/Fitness Facilities That Impacted the Industry

Turnverein, Germany (1811)

The first athletic and social club to offer organized gymnastic and athletic exercise to the masses. Founded by Frederick Ludwig Jahn, Turnverein clubs grew to as many as 150 by the middle of the 1800's, with the first Turnverein facility in the United States opening around 1848. Turnverein is credited with introducing German-style gymnastics to the West.

Triatt's Gym, Paris, France (1848)

The first indoor free-standing gym to offer members organized group classes, including classes conducted with barbells. Triatt's was the first gym to offer an extensive array of globe barbells, in addition to the standard dumbbells, Indian clubs, rings, ladders and related gymnastic equipment. In addition, Triatt's was the first gym to sell shares to raise funds for the operation of its business (sold over 250,000 shares at five francs each), and, in turn, permit those shares to be redeemed by facility members towards either private lessons or membership fees.

Boston YMCA (1850)

The Boston YMCA is often credited as being the first facility to offer a membership-based fitness gymnasium in the United States.

The Boston YMCA is often credited as being the first facility to offer a membership-based fitness gymnasium in the United States. At the time of its opening, it had the most extensively outfitted gymnasium in the U.S. The Boston YMCA established a template for the development of gymnasiums in other YMCAs throughout the world, setting a framework that the Chicago YMCAs and the London YMCA used in establishing their gymnasiums.

New York Athletic Club (1868)

The New York Athletic Club (NYAC) was co-founded by three athletes: William Curtis, John Babcock and Henry Buermeyer. The club's mission when founded was to bring order out of the chaos of the times, especially as it applied to standardized rules for athletic endeavors and the documentation of official records. The founders were the first to enforce an uncompromising approach to recording feats of athletic prowess using stopwatch, tape measure and scales. The initial club facilities were located in a small flat at 200 Sixth Avenue and 14th Street. During its early years of existence, the club was commonly referred to as number 200. Over those early years' the great athletes of the period would make pilgrimages to the small flat to test their skills in an effort to establish an official record. By 1867 the three founders raised enough money to actively market the club in various New York newspapers, eventually bringing in additional members that lead to the creation of the first by-laws in

1868. Eventually the club moved to its current location on Central Park South, becoming possibly the most well recognized athletic club in the world. The NYAC offered a blend of athletics, fitness and social ambiance that attracted not only the great athletes of the times, but also the well-heeled businessmen of the time. Today, the NYAC remains a bastion of fitness, athletic performance and social networking. Once desperate for members and short on cash, the club now has a waiting list for membership and generates revenues in excess of $35 million annually.

Hemenway Gymnasium, Harvard (1888)

Hemenway Gymnasium was the first university-based gymnasium in the United States. At the time of its opening, fitness professionals claimed it was the best outfitted gymnasium of its kind in the U.S. Hemenway Gymnasium was the first gym to offer its members access to "exercise machines." The founding director of the gym, Dudley Allen Sargent, developed and innovative series of 36 distinct exercise machines that were designed to isolate and train the body using variable resistance. At one time, the gym had a total of 56 machines. In addition to laying claim to the first gym to offer variable-resistance exercise machines, Hemenway also featured an exceptionally large assortment of dumbbells, Indian clubs, and barbells.

Hippolyte Triat's gym in the 1840s

Attila's Athletic Studio and School of Physical Culture, New York (1894)

Some historians consider Leo Durlacher's facility to be the first "gym" in the United States. While other clubs were opened in the U.S. prior to Durlacher's, his was the first facility that was dedicated totally to training men, and later women, who were interested in advanced physical culture and strength training. Attila's Studio was possibly the best equipped gym of its time, offering a full array of dumbbells, barbells, pulley's and related gymnastic equipment. In addition, the Studio was one of the first gym's to make use of carpets and mirrors. The Studio became the gym of choice for the great athletes, celebrities and performers of the era. After Durlacher's death, Sig Klein operated Attila's Studio before creating his own studio in 1926, called Sig Klein's, which subsequently became the most well-known of the early gyms and operated for over 50 years.

Vic Tanny's Health Clubs, Los Angles (1947)

Vic Tanny, and his brother, Armand, opened the first chain of modern health clubs in 1947. The Tannys introduced middle-class America to a new club model, one that pioneered the concept of a facility for men and women who were interested in pursuing a more attractive appearance and a healthier body. The Vic Tanny's club chain also introduced the fitness industry, as well as the public, to membership sales practices (e.g., membership contracts, hard sales, etc.) that continue to be a mainstay of many facilities in the industry in the 21st century. Vic Tanny's was the first chain of clubs to operate over 100 locations, and to achieve (by 2010 standards) $100 million in annual revenues.

A Vic Tanny's gym

Health and Tennis Corporation (aka Bally Total Fitness), Chicago (1962)

Established by a former employee of Vic Tanny, Don Wildman, Health and Tennis took the Vic Tanny concept to an entirely new level. Health and Tennis did not become Bally until two decades later, and subsequently Bally Total Fitness until approximately 30 years after the founding of the Health and Tennis Corporation. Bally Health and Tennis expanded on the co-ed facility concept created by Vic Tanny's, and later enhanced by Ray Wilson's clubs. The company was an industry pioneer when it came to using the acquisition of dominant regional club chains (i.e. Vic Tanny's, President's Health and Racquet, European Health Spas, Holiday Universal, etc.) to establish a national presence. In time, it became the largest chain of clubs in the world. Bally was also the first club chain in the fitness industry to be purchased by a non-industry firm, and the first club company to be traded on the public markets. Bally was also the first company in the fitness industry to run national advertisement campaigns through multiple media outlets (paper, magazines, and television), and the first group to tie its marketing success to relationships with celebrities.

Bally Total Fitness facility

Clark Hatch GX facility in Korea

Clark Hatch Fitness Centers, Asia (1965)

Clark Hatch Fitness Centers were pioneers in bringing western-style health/ fitness clubs to Asia, when their founder, Clark Hatch, opened his first club in Tokyo in 1965. He is often (and appropriately) referred to as the "Ambassador of Fitness to Asia." Clark Hatch Fitness Centers were the first "modern western-style gyms" to blossom in the Asian market. Furthermore, they were the pioneers of hotel-based fitness centers, having developed and expanded their chain of clubs through unique relationships with large hotels serving the Asian expatriate population. At one time, Clark Hatch Fitness Centers were the largest chain of health clubs in Asia.

Midtown Tennis Club, Chicago (1969)

Founded by industry legend Alan Schwartz and his father, Kevie, the Midtown Tennis Club became the first indoor tennis club in the U.S. The Midtown Tennis Club was the first of its kind in the health/fitness facility industry. It was also the first club facility to actually establish a trademarked and patented tennis program, called Tennis in No Time. The Midtown Club also became a template for future multipurpose sports clubs when it converted a portion of its tennis space into other athletic uses.

Midtown Tennis Club facility under construction in the 1960s

24 Hour Fitness, California (1983)

Originally founded in 1983 by Mark Mastrov, 24 Hour Fitness has gone on to become one of the two largest health/fitness club operators in the world, with over 400 clubs in the U.S. and Asia. 24 Hour Fitness established a template for 24/7 fitness clubs, as well as creating a standardized template for building a true national brand. 24 Hour Fitness is most recognized for being the first club company in the industry to leverage a partnership with private equity, raising both equity and debt to fuel multiple regional acquisitions and rapid organic growth to establish a dynasty of clubs. 24 Hour Fitness was one of the first club companies to develop celebrity-branded clubs (e.g., Magic Johnson, Andre Agassi, Jackie Chan, Derek Jeter, etc.). Ultimately, what most industry professionals will remember about 24 Hour Fitness is the fact that it achieved the largest sale price of any club chain in the world when it sold for $1.6 billion in 2005.

LifeTime Fitness, Minnesota (1990)

Founded in 1990 by Bahram Akradi, Lifetime established a new brand and business model for the industry. Opening its first club in 1992, Lifetime Fitness would quickly become the Best Buy or Target of fitness, creating a standardized and scalable suburban "big-box" model of facilities that could be successfully replicated. The company established a brand promise built around large full-service facilities (typically encompassing over 100,000 square feet in space and serving an entire family at an affordable price). Lifetime Fitness introduced the industry to large kid's clubs, indoor pools with water slides, enormous fitness floors with over 300 pieces of equipment, and facilities that looked the same no matter where they were located. Over the decade of the 90s (they officially became Lifetime, Inc. in 1998), they became an industry sensation. In many cases, Lifetime caused independent club operators to change the way they did business. Lifetime may be remembered longest for its successful IPO in 2001, and for being the only U.S. based fitness company to have a highly prosperous run on the public markets.

> In many cases, Lifetime caused independent club operators to change the way they did business.

Fitness First, London, England (1993)

Fitness First, founded by Mike Balfour in 1993, created a unique and successful brand built around the promise of "affordable and convenient fitness" for the masses. Each of the company's clubs featured a facility with approximately 15,000 to 20,000 square feet (1,500 to 2,000 meters) that had a gym, changing areas, a group studio, and a children's crèche. One of the unique factors that differentiated the brand was the opportunity to rent videos, which allowed members to actually select and rent videos from the clubs. Fitness First literally became the "neighborhood" club. It was the first club company in the UK and Europe to develop a scalable club business model. Fitness First was also adept at working financial markets to raise funds, which enabled it to fund its rapid organic growth. The growth was so rapid during the first several

A Fitness First club in Germany

years that Fitness First became the first British club company to float on the alternative market. In 1998, Fitness First also became the first British company to penetrate other mainland European markets. Later on, it also entered markets in both Asia and Australia. At the present time, Fitness First has more clubs in more global markets than any other company in the health/fitness facility industry, and generates more revenues than all club companies in the world, but 24 Hour Fitness.

Curves, Texas (1992)

Curves was founded in 1992 by Gary and Diane Heavin, in Harlington, Texas. Curves introduced the fitness facility industry to the power and financial potential of creating a highly branded niche club model. Curves pioneered the concept of a 30-minute express facility that catered to the needs of a niche audience, in this instance, women. The Curves model featured a small, intimate, non-intimidating setting that offered women a structured 30-minute workout, encompassing both resistance training and cardiovascular activity. Curves' motto of "no make-up and no men" became the calling card of the brand, which allowed it to penetrate an entirely new demographic that other fitness facilities had been unable to capture to that point. By 2005, Curves was an international sensation and the fastest-growing franchise operation in the world, boasting 7,000 franchised clubs. The success of Curves can be attributed not only to its ability to develop a brand that appealed to the social, emotional, and physical needs of an untapped population of adults who wished to exercise (e.g., women slightly overweight and over 30), but also to its franchise model that gave entrepreneurs the opportunity to start a business with a relatively low amount of capital. Curves was the forerunner for future franchise models, such as Anytime Fitness and Snap Fitness.

Nine Remarkable Facilities and Club Organizations That Helped Shape the Industry

Red Lerelle's Health and Racquet Club, Lafayette, Louisianna (1963)

Red's first opened its doors in 1963 as a 4,000 square foot bodybuilding gym. Over its 47-year existence, its owner, Red Lerelle, has expanded the club into a 185,000 square foot multipurpose club on 20 acres, serving over 12,000 members. Red's facilities include an outdoor water park with a lazy river, indoor pool, six indoor tennis courts, outdoor tennis courts, four indoor racquetball courts, a squash court, numerous group-exercise studios, a large fitness area, a gym, and an outdoor boot-camp area. A unique underlying practice of Red's, and one that many in the industry have tried to emulate, is to add one new element every month. This core practice has allowed Red's to continually evolve over the decades. The most amazing aspect of the club is not its 47 years of continuous operations, but the fact that the club's current membership base represents just over 10% of the entire population of Lafayette (population of 113,656), despite the existence of over 20 other clubs that serve essentially the same market.

Lucile Roberts Health Clubs, New York (1970)

Lucile Roberts developed the first chain of women's-only health/fitness clubs. The chain was the first company to appreciate the value of providing women with a non-intimidating environment for exercising (clubs before Lucile Roberts were either predominately used by men or co-ed facilities where women worked out on alternate days). Roberts' facilities featured an environment that was targeted to women and provided services that were important to women, including group exercising and "babysitting" services. The Lucile Roberts clubs also offered educational opportunities to help women achieve their professional ambitions. Lucile Roberts Health Clubs continue to operate today as a women's-only chain of clubs and is the largest women's-only club chain in the world (with the exception of Curves, which is a franchise model of express clubs for women).

> Lucile Roberts developed the first chain of women's-only health/fitness clubs.

Kings Court, Minneapolis, Minnesota (1970)

Kings Court is believed to be the first facility built specifically for the fledgling game of racquetball. The owners originally developed the club to serve men only, but soon realized that women also were interested in racquetball. As a result, the decision was made to add a women's locker room to the facility. Kings Court became the impetus for the rapid development of dedicated racquet court facilities throughout the country, including reknown clubs such as Mel Gorham's in Oceanside, California; Ken Rosland's club in Edina, Minnesota; John Wineman's Court House in Chicago, Illinois; Pat McPharland's club in Detroit, Michigan; and Chuck Spalding's club in St. Louis, Missouri.

Cedardale Health & Fitness, Haverhill, MA (1971)

Orignally developed as a four-court indoor tennis club, Cedardale went on to pioneer the multi-sport club format. Over the years, owners Dale Dibble and Ed and Zoe Veasey, expanded the club into a 175,000 square foot complex that includes ten indoor tennis courts, six racquetball courts, three indoor basketball courts, an outdoor water park (pools, slides and sprayground), a minature golf complex, ball fields, and a family pavilion. The largest multipurpose club in New England, Cedardale also pioneered the use of software for managing its business, and was one of the first clubs to offer clubs within a club.

Konami Sports and Life, Tokyo, Japan (1973)

Konami, or at the time it was founded, the People Company, was the first Asian-based company to open modern fitness clubs in the Asian market. While Clark Hatch Fitness Centers may have been the first club organization to enter the market, Konami Sports and Life was the first Asian-owned-and-operated fitness club company. The organization has since become the largest Asian-operated chain of clubs, managing over 300 clubs in Japan.

East Bank Club, Chicago (1980)

The East Bank Club was opened in 1980, initially as an indoor tennis and racquet club, and subsequently as a multipurpose fitness and sport club. East Bank was one of the first mega-clubs of the modern era, and possibly the largest, offering 450,000 square feet of space for the pursuit of every imaginable form of fitness and sport activity. East Bank also holds the distinction, along possibly with the Harbour Club of London, the Houstonian of Houston, and the Reebok Club of New York, as a landmark location that most cab drivers know of by name. In addition, the East Bank Club is the only single health/fitness club to ever achieve $50 million in annual revenues.

The East Bank Club

A David Lloyd Leisure center

David Lloyd Leisure, London, England (1982)

In 1982, possibly the most well-known and highly respected club chain in Europe, David Lloyd Leisure, was founded in the UK. David Lloyd was a British Davis Cup tennis player who leveraged his reputation to create what still is one of the most respected names in UK fitness. The first David Lloyd club combined the unique elements of racquet sports (tennis and squash), dining, fitness, and social engagement of the members. Over the next decade, David Lloyd became the leading brand of fitness and racquet clubs in England. In 1995, the company caused a huge sensation in the fitness industry when it was sold for a substantial sum of money (at the time, the largest amount ever generated by the sale of a fitness club) to Whitbread, PLC, a large publically traded company. Currently, the company owns and operates over 85 clubs, with annual revenues approaching $500 million.

Sports Club/LA, Los Angeles (1987)

In 1987, Michael Talla and Nanette Pattee Francini founded the Sports Club/LA in Century City, California. Sports Club/LA was a 100,000 square foot club that targeted the highly affluent "ME" audience of Hollywood and Southern California. It was the first fitness club where being seen often took precedence over working out. The club took on a uniquely celebrity feel, one based on a celebrity personality and one that featured a narcissist atmosphere that catered to the rich and famous, as well as to the aspiring rich and famous. The club was one of the first facilities to offer entertaining classes that were taught by celebrity instructors, as well as personal training services, physical therapy, quality dining, and designer pro shops, among other features. It was the first club chain to introduce high price initiation fees, costly monthly dues, and outlandish personal training prices, all of which they were able to command due to the perceived quality experience they delivered.

McFit, Germany (1997)

McFit was founded in 1997 by Rainer Schaller. At the time, McFit was just another new club on the market. Over the next 10 years, however, it evolved into one of the hottest club models on the market, establishing an entirely new club operating model, referred to in Europe as a no-frills, low-cost gym in the United States, such a facility is thought of as a high volume low price club. Schaller's club model was based on delivering a convenient, user-friendly, no-frills, high-tech and extremely affordable club model to the masses. McFit is currently the largest and fastest growing club company in Germany and Europe. In turn, it has spurred the development of similar club models throughout Europe and the U.S. The McFit model was one of the first club companies to incorporate a low-staff business model (typically, one staff member is on duty at all times who works reception, sells memberships, and provides assistance to members), along with a high-tech approach to member service, member communications and club operations. McFit is the first club chain to successfully incorporate technology to perform the work that is typically performed by staff members in other club models. As such, it provides no extra services for its 17 Euro monthly dues. Even taking a shower is an additional charge at Mcfit.

A McFit Club

In Their Own Words: Testimonials for Industry Icon Augie Nieto

It has been said that the only thing that lasts is the impact that we have had on other people. As such, the true definition of a successful life must include serving others. It could easily be argued that no attribute better or more clearly defines Augie Nieto. A visionary, a doer, a decision-maker…Augie inspired an entire industry to see the invisible, to achieve the unexpected, and to strive for the impossible.

This chapter features a series of heartfelt testimonials about an individual— Augie Nieto, who had an immeasurable impact on both themselves and the industry that they serve. Their thoughts and words reflect the fact that Augie led an entire industry by example. His passion and insights were the lubricant of the industry's success.

Testimonials

"In a most primary way, Augie Nieto helped create and advance into our daily world the growth and relevancy of the fitness product industry....I know, I was there, competing, and watching while he won."

John Aglialoro
CEO, Cybex International

"Augie is as responsible as anyone for the growth and expansion of the fitness industry and more specifically, for making fitness available to people of all walks of life in all parts of the world. As an entrepreneur, he is a legend, one of the few who achieved 'rock star' status and the acknowledged celebrity of being known, like Cher and Madonna and Sting...by only one name. You only have to say 'Augie.' It's a brand of its own. For me personally, I will never forget your passion and vulnerability...nor will I ever forget the honesty, integrity and class you show. You taught us all another lesson...winning not losing...leading with character...inspiring us to higher ground. Augie, thank you for being that friend for all of us! I know you know...we are always here for you."

Chip Baird
North Castle Partners

"Augie's transformation from an ALS victim to "living the happiest days of his life" will always be a tremendous source of inspiration for me. In the days following his diagnosis, Augie's world was one of despair. He was searching for hope and trying to grasp a future. He could not fathom how this could have happened to him. ALS imposed itself on someone whose life's story, up to that point, was one of rapid achievement and success with very few humbling experiences. Augie simply didn't know how to write the last chapter of a very meaningful life. Overwhelmed with self–pity, he attempted suicide with a pill overdose. I visited him in the hospital shortly after he woke up, right at the time he was starting to discover a whole new reason to live. Augie has been a wonderful friend for over 30 years, However, starting with that visit he has become so much more. Through his eyes, I too am now experiencing life with a new understanding. My friendship with Augie has left a profound impact I will feel for the rest of my life.

With the amazing love and encouragement from his wife, Lynne, his children, and his large circle of friends, Augie took charge and began building a life with a new purpose. He founded Augie's Quest and wrote two books. A whole new community has gravitated around him. He has devoted himself to fellow ALS patients offering comfort, support and guidance. He continues to serve on the boards of Octane Fitness and Quest Software."

Peter Brown
President, Athletic Business

"From day one, Augie has used his incredible drive and will to win to make an indelible mark on the industry."

Paul Byrne
CEO, Precor

———————————————

"Augie Nieto was a true innovator. He did not just create an exercise bike—he created the cardiovascular equipment category. And that category really helped develop the whole health club industry. He did not stop at one product but went on to develop an array of cardiovascular offerings, strength equipment, free weights and a major equipment company. But, he is credited for being a vital force in developing IHRSA as a trade association and influencing the overall growth of fitness facility users. We are all indebted to Augie's contributions and leadership. But, probably what we owe him more is his role as a leader advancing medical science to cure a disease—an effort that will impact many who follow him. He truly has created a legacy of large footprints."

Rick Caro
President, Management Vision, Inc.

———————————————

"A few years ago I was contacted by a West Coast publication for comment on Augie Nieto's impact on the fitness world. The most honest thing I could tell the reporter then was that in my opinion, Augie Nieto was the 'Henry Ford of the fitness industry.' That's still my opinion, I can add one thing. Back in the early 1980s, I was one of Ray Wilson's and Augie Nieto's early customers when I acquired 66 Lifecycles for my two clubs in Atlanta. I can say for sure that those yellow, blue, red, and white Lifecycles energized my clubs and my members just loved them. Today, it's amazing to look back on the story of how Augie, as a college kid with a great entrepreneurial spirit, took the opportunity of working with Ray Wilson on Lifecycle to go on and hit a true home-run in the fitness industry worldwide, a home-run now called Life Fitness. Way to go, Augie! We love you!"

Norm Cates
Publisher, *Club Insider*, since 1993
www.clubinsideronline.com

———————————————

"My perspective on Augie is not so much about him as a business person but as a person. I had known of Augie and his accomplishments over the course of his life. I know achieving great goals and financial success goes a long way in defining a person. But, I think we all realize that's only one small piece of who a man truly is. My greatest recollection of Augie is seeing him in a food court in a mall in California. I was visiting the area when our paths crossed. What struck me was his genuine warmth. But, maybe more importantly, it was the interaction with his relatively young children that caught my attention. He was such a loving father. I had the opportunity to see the real Augie. That's when I realized he was much more than a success in business."

Joe Cirulli
Founder and CEO, Gainesville Health & Racquet

"I first met Augie in Finland on the Life Fitness 'Premier Club' trip, an event that recognized those Life Fitness sales staff who achieved 10% over their targets. He had a profound effect on me that's still with me today.

As a new boy on the block, we exchanged a few light-hearted batters regarding others within our party. Needles to say, as the boss, he requested the fasted snowmobile, and we were instructed to keep inline, one after each other!!! As soon as we hit open space, it was mayhem (last one back bought the beers).

The words he gave to me back then, after being strapped up by the hospital just before attending our dinner party and just prior to being flown back to the USA for surgery have always stayed with me. He said 'have fun with Life Fitness, make sure you hit your targets, and you will fit in just fine here at Life Fitness. Also, don't forget I'm the boss!'

From there, the famous four F's of fitness were developed: Fitness, Fun, Fat loss & Friends. I can confirm through meeting Augie and the fantastic team at Life Fitness, I have made some of the best friends for Life."

Rob Chorlton
Principal, Leisure Solutions

"Augie has been a great friend, both personally and professionally for most of the last 30 years. In my view, his introduction of the Lifecycle to the commercial club market was the game changer that brought CV equipment and training to the forefront in clubs. Prior to that time, most clubs were focused almost exclusively on strength training and what CV offerings that were available were limited to a few self-propelled treadmills and some very antiquated and boring stationary bikes. The Lifecycle brought technology and entertainment to fitness. While the fitness industry will always be grateful to Augie for his unwavering support, he has always been there for the industry when the industry has needed him, Augie's greatest legacy will be how he has revolutionized how research is conducted for ALS. In conjunction with the Muscular Dystrophy Association and the Cambridge, Mass-based Therapy Development Institute, Augie and his team have redefined the way ALS research is conducted. Under Augie's leadership and inspiration, they have developed a cure-driven initiative that has helped coordinate ALS research and testing across the globe. This business model is nimble and extremely efficient, and has produced some remarkable results to date. As Augie has always been there for the industry, I am gratified to see how the industry continues to be there for Augie, when he needs us the most."

Art Curtis, PhD
CEO, Millennium Sports Club Management
Chairman, IHRSA 2010–2011

"It is very hard to describe the enormous impact that Augie Nieto and Life Fitness have had on the evolution of the health and fitness industry in only a few words.

I think it is true to say that most people do not like exercise. We, as an industry, continue to strive to make exercise more enjoyable, more fun, more engaging and simply to just try and 'make the medicine taste better.' With the introduction of the first computerized bike, the Lifecycle, Augie took the first major steps to introduce the elements into the modern-day health and fitness clubs. Despite a tough beginning, Augie went on to found and grow what has become the largest fitness company in the world. As the man behind the company, Augie has always lived 'by example' and been a very passionate, driving force to help the industry to grow where it is today.

I congratulate Augie for his wonderful insight and drive, especially in the last few years, as he has shown all of us the most amazing qualities, demonstrating how to live to the fullest, despite the cards we have been dealt in life.

We love and admire you Augie."

Tony de Leede
Founder of Cardio Theater
Former Managing Director, Fitness First Australia

"Dear Augie; The enormous growth our industry has enjoyed these past 30 years would not have been possible without your leadership and the support of your company, Life Fitness. When I look back on the early days, when Bally Manufacturing first introduced the Lifecycle, followed soon thereafter by the Life Rower, and then the Life Step, I realize how lucky our members were to have access to such innovative equipment. You and Life Fitness have truly made fitness fun! I also remember when you first launched the Life Rower, you gave away a Lancer (car) to a lucky buyer. That winner was me, Augie, so thanks once again! My fondest memories in the fitness business took place in the 80s and 90s, when you and John McCarthy were front and center, telling all of us that a 'high tide floats all boats.' This is a mantra I have lived by. I have always tried to support my peers and share best practices, so we all grow stronger together.

Thanks for all you have done to make our industry such an exciting and rewarding one."

Geoff Dyer
Founder and Chairman, Lifestyle Family Fitness

"My long friendship with Augie began in 1980, in Atlanta, far away from my home, with two yellow Lifecycles. Augie asked me to include these Lifecycles in my club, on spec. 'They will totally change the fitness industry,' he told me. Not only that—he also assured me that this equipment could help get people in shape in just 12 minutes! I figured I had to try these. In Canada, GoodLife was the first club to have Lifecycles, and since then, we have been one of Augie's biggest supporters, as the inspiration he has brought to us goes far beyond just Lifecycles.

Augie's genius is that he knows how to keep things simple and that people need to find do-able solutions that create optimism for the future of their health. This is exactly the approach he is taking also with his quest to find the cure for ALS—he seeks to instill both commitment and hope that this terrible disease will ultimately be defeated. He is superb at getting people on board, no matter what the challenge is!

I am so proud to count him as a friend, and I am awed by the dedication he brings to his cause. The fitness industry would not be the same without Augie."

David Patchell Evans
Founder and CEO, GoodLife Fitness, Canada

"It was 1980, and we had just opened the Telegraph Hill Club, when Augie called to introduce himself. I had already heard of Augie because of his nearly singlehanded development of a new fitness center at our shared alma mater, Claremont Men's College. His reason for calling was to offer us a free one-month trial of a new product, the Lifecycle, which we could buy at the end of the trial if we liked it. I doubted that it would succeed, but agreed that he could bring us one. He drove up the coast to San Francisco and personally delivered the bike. The trial began and our members took to it right away. The problem was that we had already spent our capital dollars for the year, and we couldn't afford to buy it. Augie drove up and picked up the bike. He later told me that we were the only company to ask him to pick up their trial Lifecycle.

Of course, we went on to buy hundreds of his products over the years. The company prospered under Augie's entrepreneurial genius, his commitment to excellence, and his impeccable ethics. And he has never let up; working just as hard finding a cure for ALS as he did in those first years delivering bikes club to club. He has been an inspiration to everyone who has had the privilege to know him."

Jim Gerber
Co-founder, Western Athletic Clubs

"Augie's vision quest for Lifecycle and the positive effect it would have on the industry and consumers was incredibly spot on…he most certainly created extraordinary results from ordinary resources, and the growth and popularity of the Lifecycle helped accelerate the expansion of the fitness industry. My personal opportunity to help Augie expand the Lifecycle intellectual property and direct the production of Lifecircuit was an experience I will carry for a lifetime and learned first-hand, what a warrior he was then and through his ultimate life's challenge continues to be. It is with great admiration that I write this testimonial…"

Ken Germano
Executive Director, Medical Fitness Association

"I have had the pleasure of knowing Augie for over 30 years, and there is no doubt that he will be written up in the history books as one of the true pioneers and Godfathers of the fitness industry. While his business success and acumen is both proven and very impressive, it is in fact his courage, leadership, and zest for life that have inspired me the most. Augie is a giant of a man, and my life has been significantly advanced by having him and his amazing wife, Lynne, in it.

    With love and respect."

David Giampaolo
Managing Director, Pi Capital

"Augie's passion for his family, his passion for his craft, and his passion for Life Fitness have always been unwavering…which is why Augie's Quest has become the fitness industry's legacy in fighting ALS. Augie has helped us all to be part of something much bigger than ourselves…I'm honored to be his friend."

Lee Guthrie
President, Lee Guthrie & Associates

"Clearly, Augie Nieto was key in recognizing the need for cardiovascular health in the early 80s. Despite adversity along the way, his vision to develop equipment for the fitness industry has advanced all of us to the nation's current levels of health and fitness today. And now, an even more monumental vision of Augie's—his quest to find a cure for ALS—will be his most noble gift to the world. Augie brought a debilitating and deadly disease to the forefront of our lives through his own mortality. I have always admired Augie's passion for life, but his intense drive and sincere dedication to finding a cure for this little-known disease is unequalled, and inspires me beyond words. Augie has led us in ways far greater than we could have ever imagined and is the pride of the fitness industry. "

Ron Hemelgarn
President, 21st Century Fitness Centers

"Everyone knows Augie's 'firsts and successes' with Life Fitness, his ability to get business done with vision, focus and dedication, his drive to burn 1,000 calories before breakfast (so he could enjoy the rest of the day's food and drink), and his enthusiasm to enjoy his work and play to the fullest. But, the thing which stands out the most for me about Augie is his ability to inspire me and others to do even better than they think they can. This inspiration comes to us through Augie's living example, his capability (directly and indirectly) to motivate others to do all that is needed to achieve more, and to do whatever you do with all your heart and soul. His passion has the power to make good things happen, and it demands that we all 'keep up.' Some may think these are examples of good business practices which Augie followed, but this wasn't only Augie's approach to business…it is his approach to life!"

John W. Holsinger
Director, IHRSA Asia Pacific
Former VP International & Managing Director, Asia Pacific, Life Fitness

"Frequently, we live our lives for Reason, but without Thought. Good friends we have for Thought, but without Reason. Augie is That Friend, who Inspires you to Be Better.

   Thank You Augie!"

Gary A Jones
Founder Inventor, Hammer Strength

"Augie's real genius was in marketing and finance. It took every bit of his genius to get people to pay $2,000 to $3,000 for a Lifecycle in the very early days, when the next closest competitor was a Monark or Tunturi bike that listed for $695. I've known Augie from his first days of selling the Lifecycle for Ray Wilson, and I still don't know how he did it. It was pure genius and a lot of hard work. He introduced electronics into our industry, pioneered its reliability, and made the Lifecycle a success and a household name, and if that wasn't enough, parlayed a single bike into the largest and most successful company in the history of our industry. He raised the bar for all of us with his innovation and competitiveness. I've learned a lot from Augie over the years, because he was always willing to share his secrets to success, even when it was with a competitor. Keiser is a better company today, because of Augie Nieto."

Dennis Keiser
President and Founder, Keiser Corporation

"For over 30 years, Augie Nieto has been a pioneer in the fitness industry. When I started Fitcorp in 1979, we had limited equipment opportunities. Stationary bikes were cumbersome and uncomfortable. Treadmills were too expensive. Strength training equipment looked like medieval torture devices. Augie changed everything! His Lifecycle made cardiovascular exercise fun, and his Life Fitness selectorized equipment made strength training exciting! Augie changed the face of the health club industry. We are all very grateful for all his contributions."

Gary Klencheski
President, Fitcorp

"As someone who has spent his entire working life (24 years) in the fitness industry, I can say I know just about everyone there is to know in this business. If there is one person's name that could be considered to have its own 'brand' it is Augie Nieto. If you are in this business, you have heard of Augie Nieto. He has 'rock star' status, meaning that you do not even have to say his full name. Just say 'Augie' to someone in the industry, and they will know who you are talking about. This status is not easily earned; it comes from creating and running an incredibly successful business and touching many lives in the process. I felt like I was meeting a celebrity the first time I met Augie and that feeling is still there when I spend time with him today."

Dennis Lee
President, Octane Fitness

"I met Augie over 30 years ago when he helped my father, Mort, host seminars to guide people into the 'court club' business. Despite Mort and Augie preaching 'multi-purpose, multi-purpose, multi-purpose,' people left the room chanting 'racquetball, racquetball, racquetball.' Within five years, those same people were knocking on Augie's door. Augie's personality, vision, and courage can be summed up in one of his statements I'll never forget: 'I want—and the industry needs—the strongest possible competitors. They will bring out the best in me, the best in my company, and the best in the industry.' Like so many others, Augie will forever be an inspiration to me, and my family. Would that and I I had a fraction of his courage!"

Chuck Leve
Executive Director, Association of Fitness Industry Retailers & Manufacturers (AFIRM)
Former Vice President, Business Development, IHRSA

"Augie Nieto has no equal when it comes to the level of impact on the global health and fitness movement. As the founder of the Life Fitness equipment company, his continued innovation for more than three decades concerning how people exercise revolutionized the commercial health and fitness business. He is a legend among us, and someone whom I am proud to call my friend."

Mark Mastrov
Chairman, New Evolution Ventures
Founder, 24 Hour Fitness Worldwide

"While I did not know Augie personally before he was stricken with ALS, his courage and work with Life Fitness are known throughout our industry. When our industry moved from very basic bikes to Lifecycles, there was a dramatic change in the consumer's perception of fitness and the innovations surrounding fitness and technology. The work Augie did to grow and enhance Life Fitness as a benchmark for credibility with health club consumers was and remains immeasurable. I believe Augie helped the industry grow not only in size, but also in credibility and authenticity. His strength, courage, tenacity, self discipline, and determination have a positive impact on his ability to cope with ALS and will indeed dramatically accelerate the cure for this disease. He is an inspiration to all in fighting the challenges that life deals and in setting a path for positive change!"

Bill McBride
COO, Club One

"For 25 years, Augie Nieto was the unbeaten, untied, undisputed heavyweight champion of the worldwide fitness industry. He achieved this distinction not simply by reason of the products that he developed, but by his intelligence, his competitiveness, his passion for the business, and, above all, by the respect and care that he tendered to every customer no matter how large or how small. No one deserves more credit for the globalization of the fitness industry than does Augie Nieto. Under his leadership, Life Fitness was the first American fitness company in Europe, the first in Asia, the first in Latin America, and in Africa and in the Middle East. All the rest of us followed in the trail that he had blazed. But, his Olympian achievements as a business leader pale in comparison to the raw courage, determination, dedication, and devotion that he and his wife, Lynne have exemplified in their commitment to the cure of ALS since he was struck down with that terrible disease. All of us who have known Augie feel the same way. We feel privileged to call him a friend."

John McCarthy
Former Executive Director, IHRSA

"Everyone involved with IHRSA and the club business knows the Augie legend. You need only to say his first name, and immediately, you see the recognition and respect in the eyes of those around you. His story is that of a modern-day hero, who has been beset by tribulations that have served to strengthen his will and have driven him to embark on a great quest. His quest has resulted in the most exciting breakthroughs in the history of ALS research. His battle continues, but he never falters and never wavers. He always projects the goodwill and positive spirit of a man who comes from this wonderful industry. I'm proud to call him my friend."

Joe Moore
President & CEO, IHRSA

"Augie Nieto launched his career by transforming the stationary bike into a computerized tool designed to improve cardiovascular health and fitness. In the process, he revolutionized the entire health club industry by creating a total-body solution of exercise equipment innovations that endure to this day. Augie has now decreed his legacy by turning a personal tragedy into a global opportunity to help others. He inspires us with his determination to find a cure for a seemingly incurable disease. He challenges us to open our wallets and our hearts in his crusade to defeat an illness that has felled many, but has compelled him and his family to the most selfless of missions—making a difference in the lives of others. Augie, while we have always been impressed with your larger-than-life personality and have always tried to emulate your successful career, we are truly mesmerized by and grateful for the legacy you have bestowed on us through Augie's Quest."

Mike Motta
President & CEO, Plus One Health Management, New York, NY

"Augie inspired me back in 1985 when I first met him, as he began setting up European operations for Life Fitness. He motivated by example, supported the team, and remained a genuine person that I admired. Augie's initial support of IHRSA's European Club Leaders Conference in the late 90s created many opportunities and helped cross-border relations, whose positive effects are still being felt. He will be remembered by me and many veterans of the industry beyond the borders of the USA."

Hans Muench
Director of Europe, IHRSA

"Augie's commitment to selling the Lifecycle, in many ways, made the modern gym a reality. He saw the enormous potential that bringing weight training and cardio exercise together under one roof had—and he innately understood the value of product 'sizzle' to the fledgling industry. In so many ways, the introduction of the Lifecycle into gyms was the 'tipping point' for the modern fitness business."

Frank Napolitano
President, Globalfit

"In the mid 1980s, I was doing research on advanced cardio equipment for the commercial fitness market for Quinton Instrument Company. During a swing to the West Coast, I had a chance to talk to some fitness influencers, including Joe Gold, at World Gym, managers at the home office of Gold's Gyms, and others in the industry. To illustrate the marketplace, I had heard the same story during many of the interviews. The story of Augie and his van taking the early version of the lifecycle around to gym owners to try to get a trial or at least to show it to customers and to get feedback on this 'future of the fitness market.' Many credited Augie and his perseverance and sales efforts as the start of the modern fitness industry, as we know it today. Later in the 1990s, when I had a chance to first meet Augie, it was obvious that the early struggles were an important milestones that helped him and the organizations that he led to become some of the most successful in our industry. His perseverance continues."

Stan Peterman
Former Director of Sales, Quinton

"My respect for Augie Nieto goes well beyond the role he has played in the development of the modern-day fitness industry to one so personal it would be difficult to put on paper. His legacy may be that that he is most responsible for bringing aerobic exercise into a worldwide accepted indoor activity. He began his challenge as a young man, who kept his eyes on the prize and never waivered in his beliefs. This same commitment continues to this day. Augie's entrepreneurial spirit and high regard for others remain unchallenged. His integrity and self-discipline are watermarks for which we should all aspire. No accolades can express the positive impact he has had on me over our 25-year relationship."

Bill Pearl
Former Mr. America and Mr. Universe

"I first met Augie around 1980 at Paramount's offices in Los Angeles, soon after we both entered the fitness industry. Although I don't recall the exact date, I clearly remember the meeting and how impressed I was with him. His level of enthusiasm was amazing, and his professionalism at such an early stage of his career told me that he would be a difference maker. What Augie accomplished while at Life Fitness has, without question, had a dynamic influence on our entire industry and one that is lasting. We have all benefited. His quest over the past few years is beyond just inspirational and makes all of us who consider Augie a friend or colleague proud to know him. To use a sports analogy, if there is ever a Fitness Industry Hall of Fame, Augie will be unanimously voted in on the first ballot."

Steve Rhodes
President, Paramount Fitness Corporation

"If I have to illustrate Augie's talent as a leader and his influence on myself and the management team at Life Fitness, it is through the words *'self knowledge.'* Augie, like all of us and particularly like all entrepreneurs, is a very stubborn and determined person…but not to the point where it becomes self-defeating. Augie—who is an extremely talented individual himself—had a remarkable talent to gather a management team of individuals around him who complemented himself, enforced, and challenged him. He picked people who were better at certain aspects of the business than Augie himself. That is a rare talent. He also could step aside and let his team run with the ball on stage….mostly when he could stay in control behind the curtain…. There is a modern management hype called 'Servant Leadership.' In my humble opinion, Augie is the epitome of that leadership style!

On a personal note, Augie has been—as long as I have known him—a true 'Work Hard—Play Hard' guy; always in for some fun; he loves a party. He also was a great buddy for me in running. We have covered many hundreds of miles all over the world together, and he was my inspiration to run my first marathon in Chicago in 2000.

As a European, I really admire Augie's ability to really *think globally*. He was the driving force in making Life Fitness the first fitness company with a true worldwide presence."

Herman Rutgers
Executive Director, European Health & Fitness Association
Former Executive Vice-President, Commercial Fitness, Life Fitness

"While I knew of Augie during my career in the fitness industry, it wasn't until the IHRSA Bash five years ago, that I really got to know Augie. Ray Wilson was sitting next to me that evening and shared the story of how Augie brought the Lifecycle to life by selling bikes out of the back of his van. I spent time talking to Augie that evening, and I felt like we had known each other our whole lives….he had that ability to make each person feel special. Like many leading innovators, Augie was also a dreamer. Augie has always been obsessed with creating something special, something lasting, and something that will improve peoples lives. What impressed me the most about Augie was that he didn't stop dreaming once he was stricken with ALS. This next phase of his life, the happiest phase of his life, has enabled Augie to focus his energy and passion even more acutely, this time to help find a cure for ALS….and once again change peoples lives for the better. I know he will succeed, he always has."

Mike Sheehan
CEO, Bally Total Fitness

"I first met Augie in April of 1995 at the FIBO show in Germany. On our very first handshake, Augie made a big impression. Augie has the ability to bring out the best in people and motivate them to go 'the extra mile.' He was very instrumental in helping me to grow the business by traveling with me throughout the world and showing true leadership and global thinking! He is the most competitive person I have ever met; in business or pleasure… he is a WINNER!"

Leo Schreuders
Managing Director, Octane Fitness
Former Marketing and Sales Director of Europe, Middle East and Africa, Life Fitness

———————————

"Augie, a revered pioneer in the fitness industry, is the ultimate proof that you cannot extinguish true passion, no matter what the circumstances."

Alan Schwartz
Chairman, TCA Holdings, LLC

———————————

"I've watched Augie learn and grow by 'putting himself out there,' sometimes winning, sometimes not, but always taking the lead, despite the risk of failure. His courage and strength are traits I admire, his willingness to take on big challenges is a trait I applaud, and, his sense of humanity and humor are traits I love. He personifies the adage: 'the only failure is when you fail to try.' Augie is and always will be an inspiration to me."

Steven Schwartz
President and CEO, TCA Holdings, LLC

———————————

"There are tipping points in our personal lives and in our careers, but usually they are separate events, often many years apart. Augie, however, in a relatively short period of time, has managed to create tipping points for many of us in the industry that transcend all aspects of our lives, both personal and professional. On a personal level, he has shown us what dedication to a cause and belief in an end can create. He has shown us the true power of family and friends. On a professional level, he has set a new benchmark for the term 'determination' and the power of harnessing the collective goodwill of humans. His industry achievements pale in comparison to this. We know we are fortunate to be a part of this great industry, but it has taken Augie's challenge to bring it together. Augie's legacy to this industry is that we are now a brotherhood that can see beyond the simple competitive nature of the business to the greater whole, and as a result, we are poised to become a force to be reckoned with in health care worldwide."

Mark Smith
Chairman, Cityfitness Group
Former Chairman, TSI

"Much of the growth of Life Fitness and of the health and fitness industry, as a whole, was a direct result of the vision and passion of Augie Nieto, and I was fortunate to have had a front-row seat. It was my pleasure to work for Augie Nieto at Life Fitness during the company's early years. It was an exciting time for the industry and for Life Fitness. During that time, I was able to experience the early growth of Life Fitness, going from one product, the Lifecycle exercise bike, to a complete line of electronic exercise equipment, including the Life Rower, Life Step, and Life Circuit.

During that time, I learned a great deal working for Augie. I learned how important it was to have a passion; to have a vision; to be persistent; and to be loyal. Being around Augie, I also learned the importance of building and sustaining lasting relationships, both personally and professionally.

However, as much of an inspiration Augie's success in the fitness industry has been, he has become an even bigger inspiration to me over the past six years. The man is amazing and has done so much for so many people. He has shown me once again that if you have a vision for something, if you are passionate about something and if you are persistent, you can accomplish anything.

I am very appreciative and feel blessed to know Augie personally and to have had a chance to work for him."

Jim Swieter
Co-Founder/Managing Partner, ZOOM Sports

"I have known Augie Nieto since the early 1990s, when here in the UK, he and his Life Fitness team were extremely active in the development of the UK health and fitness industry. Augie was always open to contributions in new thinking and the innovative ideas of his clients. The result of which was the Industry Leadership Conferences around Europe, which were sponsored by Life Fitness. From his forward thinking, the EHFA was established in the early 2000s, and today, thanks to his selfless attitude, the EHFA is a thriving organization that supports the European health and fitness industry. He is a legend who stands out as a beacon in our sector. I am richer in many ways for knowing him."

Harm B Tegelaars
EHFA President

"I still remember when we at Wellbridge (originally Club Sports International) were being ground-breaking by adding racquetball, basketball, indoor pool, and a fitness component to our indoor tennis club. The cardiovascular area was no more than a hallway. Augie made a pitch to put in two of his stationary bikes vs. a Schwinn Aerodyne. The cost of his bikes were 'outrageous!' Little did we know that a year later, we would be adding a cardiovascular room and multiples of Augie's stationary bikes. He changed the industry by introducing the general public to cardiovascular training. We sometimes forget where we were on the timeline. It now seems like its always just been part of the industry. We all owe Augie a thank you for the opportunity to be part of his dream!"

Ed Williams
CEO, Wellbridge Company

"Augie Nieto has become a legend in our industry not just because of his great vision, hard work, and countless hours that he dedicated to building a great team. All of these attributes are important. While Augie and many people possess these, what has separated Augie is the fact that he cares for others. He cares for his family and friends. He cares for people who have been stricken with ALS. He cares that people can change their lives through exercise. He cares for the people who purchase his products. He cares for the people who use the products. He cares for the people who are part of his team. He has become a legend because he has the ability to get people to accomplish tasks that others see as impossible. It started with giving millions of people the hope that they could change their lives through exercise, and they have. Today, he is giving thousands of people afflicted with ALS each year the hope of a better tomorrow, and they will. Augie's legacy is secure because he cares for you and me."

Mike Zinda
Vice-President National Accounts & Latin America
Life Fitness

Books

Beyond the Universe: The Bill Pearl Story. Bill Pearl with Kim Shott. Agni Press, Jamaica, New York. 2003

Getting Stronger. Bill Pearl and Gary T. Moran. Bill Pearl and Shelter Publications, Inc.,Bolinas, CA. 1986.

Legends of the Iron Game; Volume 1. Bill Pearl, George Coates, Richard Thornley, Jr. Bill Pearl Enterprises, Inc. Phoenix, Oregon. 2010.

Muscletown USA. John Fair. Pennsylvania State University Press, University Park, Pennsylvania. 1999.

Sandow—The Mighty Monarch of Muscle. Georord Nisivoccia. Special Memorial Edition, Newark, NJ 1947.

The First Hundred Years: A Portrait of the NYAC. Bob Considine and Fred Jarvis. The Macmillan Company, Toronto, Canada. Copyright 1969 by the New York Athletic Club

The Gospel of Strength According to Sandow. T.Shaw Fitchett, Melbourne, Australia. 1902.

The Indian Club Exercise. Sim D. Kehoe. 1866.

The Way to Live in Health and Physical Fitness. George Hackenschmidt. Strength and Health Publishing. York, PA. 1934

Younger Women, Faster Airplanes, Bigger Crocodiles: The Story of Arthur Jones. John Szimanski. PDA Press, Mauldin, SC. 2003.

Articles & Courses

A Lifetime of Dance and Fitness. Amy Florence Fischbach. www.clubindustry.com

Lotte Berk: One of the Strangest and Most Ruthless Characters of the 20th Century. Cassandra Jardine. Telegraph.Co.UK. July 20, 2010.

Dudley Allan Sargent: Health Machines and the Energized Male Body. Carolyn de la Pena', University of California at Davis. Iron Game History. October 2003.

From Milo to Milo: A History of Barbells, Dumbbells and Indian Clubs. Jan Todd, PhD., University of Texas. Iron Game History, Volume 3, #6.

History of Scottish Heavy Events. Charles Black.

Jowett Institute Course in Muscle Building and Physical Culture. Jowett Institute of Physical Culture, New York, New York. 1927.

Making Broad Shoulders; Bodybuilding and Physical Culture in Chicago 1890 – 1920. David s. Churchill. History of Education Quarterly. July 2008.

References

Mighty Men of Old: Being a Gallery of Pictures and Biographies of Outstanding Old Time Strongmen. Strength and Health Magazine, Volume 1. 1940.

Progress Turnverein, Records; Records 1860 – 1976. Collection 3057. The Historical Society of Pennsylvania.

Requiem for a Strongman: Reassessing the Career of Professor Louis Attila. Jan Todd, PhD, and Kim Beckwith. University of Texas. Iron Game History.

The Classical Ideal and its Impact on the Search for Suitable Exercise 1774 – 1830. Jan Todd, PhD, University of Texas. Iron Game History. Volume 2, number 4.

The Evolution of Health Clubs. www. clubindustry.com. December 1, 1995.

The Fitness Movement and the Fitness Center Industry; 1960 – 2000. Marc Stern, Business & Economic History.

The Strength Builders: A History of Barbells, Dumbbells and Indian Clubs. Jan Todd. International Journal of the History of Sport. Volume 20, Issue 1. March 2003. Pages 65 to 90.

Newspaper Articles & Releases

New York Magazine, May 1978. An intimidating New Class: the Physical Elite

Wall Street journal, May 2, 1979

New York Times, June 12, 1985

Stars & Stripes, November 4, 1964.

General Websites

www.oldtimestrongman.com

www.sandowplus.co.uk

www.sandowmuseum.com

www.bernarmacfadden.com

www.charlesatlas.com

www.superstrengthbooks.com

www.informaworld.com/smpp/content

www.answers.com/topic/jack-la-lanne#health-clubs

www.lifetimefitness.com

www.thehistoryof.net

Stephen Tharrett, M.S.

Stephen has been involved with the fitness industry for more than three decades. He began his fitness career in 1979, when he joined the Flint YMCA, Flint, Michigan, as a fitness director. During his extensive career, Stephen has held a variety of positions in the field, including working a YMCA, corporate fitness (Chemical Bank), and the commercial fitness sector. Stephen spent 20 years with ClubCorp, a Dallas, Texas-based company that owns and operates a number of private country clubs, business clubs, and sports clubs. During his tenusre with ClubCorp, he served in several roles, including director of athletics, vice-president of athletics and tennis, and senior vice-president of athletics, tennis, and golf. In 2004, Stephen started his own company, Club Industry Consulting, which provides club owners and operators with a variety of high-level consulting services. From the summer of 2008 till the fall of 2010, he served as the Chief Executive Officer and Managing Director of the Russian Fitness Group, owners and operators of 48 clubs in Russia and a top 25 global fitness company by revenues.

From 1994 to 1997, Stephen served on the IHRSA Board and was elected as IHRSA's President in 1996. He has also been a co-editor of the 2nd, 3rd and soon to be released 4th edition of the landmark text, ACSM's Health/Fitness Facility Standards and Guidelines. In addition, Stephen has authored three other books, including Fitness Management, one of only two textbooks on the market on managing a health/fitness club.

Frank O'Rourke

Frank is a fitness-industry veteran, with over 20 years of experience in personal fitness coaching and equipment sales. Upon graduation from the University of Oklahoma, Frank began his career in fitness with Johnson and Johnson Health Management and the North Dallas Athletic Club. From 1994 to 2001, Frank successfully promoted both commercial and consumer lines of equipment with Cybex and Ground Zero, now known as Free Motion Fitness. In 2002, he joined Nautilus as a territory manager for the south central region, and won the organization's sales person of the year award in 2003. In 2004, Frank was recruited by Connell Communications, a print media company, to serve as the national sales director for its Health & Lifestyle Division.

In 2007, Frank returned to Nautilus, as the head of sales for Latin America, and was subsequently promoted to regional manager for Asia Pacific and Latin America in 2008. In 2009, Nautilus sold its commercial interest in StairMaster and Schwinn Fitness. Frank then transitioned to the new company, which was designated as StairMaster, where he currently serves as its director of international sales.

About the Authors

James A. Peterson, Ph.D., FACSM

Jim is currently the owner and publisher for two Monterey, California-based companies that produce instructional materials, Coaches Choice and Healthy Learning. From 1971–1990, he was a member of the faculty at the United States Military Academy. Subsequently, he spent five years as the director of sports medicine for StairMaster Sports/Medical Products, Inc., based in Kirkland, Washington. He is the author of more than 80 books and more than 200 published articles. He has appeared on a number of national television shows, including ABC's Good Morning America, ABC's Nightline, and the CBS Evening News. His written efforts have appeared in a variety of publications, including *The New York Times*.